General Knowledge Quizzes

General Knowledge Quizzes

by

Don Wilson

First published by *Clarion* MCMXCVI.
Some material in this book has been drawn from *The Quiz-Setter's Quiz Book*. This edition published by arrangement with Elliot Right Way Books.

Typeset in 11/13pt Times by Letterpart Ltd., Reigate, Surrey.

Printed and bound in Great Britain by Cox & Wyman Ltd., Reading, Berkshire.

Clarion: published from behind no. 80 Brighton Road, Tadworth, Surrey, England.

Contents

Dedication

To Pete and Robin,
with whom I've had much success at quizzes.

Introduction

Whether you set quizzes on a regular basis or simply enjoy taking part in them, this is the book for you.

If you set quizzes, you know that there comes a time when you are pushed to find questions: this book will solve that problem. You can either use quizzes en bloc from this book, or simply pick and choose particular questions from different quizzes to supplement your own questions.

If you enjoy participating, then you can derive a great deal of enjoyment from this book either by asking yourself the questions while keeping the answers covered or by having a friend or relative ask you the questions.

As you will know, most quiz books usually have the answers overleaf or at the end of the book, and as a result it is very easy to associate the wrong answer with a question unless you check very carefully. You will not have that problem with this book.

There are 3500 questions waiting for you: enjoy!

Don Wilson

Quiz Rounds

Quiz 1

1. Which one word means a wind instrument, a cavalry officer (formerly) and an ice-cream holder? **Cornet**

2. What nationality is golfer Costantino Rocca? **Italian**

3. What term is used to describe the situation where you owe more on your mortgage than your house is worth? **Negative Equity**

4. On TV, who presents *It'll Be Alright On the Night*? **Denis Norden**

5. Which is the largest city in Canada? **Toronto**

6. What would you find in a clocher? **Bells (It is a belfry.)**

7. Francis Drake reputedly set up a brass plate in what is now California, naming the land what? **New Albion**

8. True or false: a Clouded Yellow is a butterfly? **True**

9. Who had successive Number Ones in 1993 with *Pray*, *Relight My Fire* and *Babe*? **Take That**

10. What sort of creature is a natterjack? **Toad**

11. On which play was the musical *My Fair Lady* based? ***Pygmalion***

12. What, to an Australian, is a Dinnyhayser? A sheep shearer, a knock-out punch or a two pint glass? **Knock-out Punch**

13. Who played Sid James' wife in the TV series *Bless This House*? **Diana Coupland**

14. What is the capital of Paraguay? **Asuncion**

15. What is the epicarp of an orange? **The peel**

16. Who was the first player to score 100 Premier League goals in England? **Alan Shearer**

17. Which writer married Nora Barnacle in 1931, suffered from glaucoma and died in Zurich after an operation for an ulcer in 1941? **James Joyce**

18. Which historical character was played in films by Bette Davis, Flora Robson and Jean Simmons? **Elizabeth I**

19. Which country contains continental Europe's only active volcanoes? **Italy**

20. What nationality is tennis player Javier Frana? **Argentinian**

Quiz 2

1. Who would use a glaive? An artist, a soldier or a conjuror? **A soldier (It is a weapon.)**

2. Who were the Fuggers? Smugglers, bankers or politicians? **Bankers**

3. What are O'Donohue's White Horses? **Foaming waves**

4. True or false: Boötes is a constellation in the Northern Hemisphere? **True**

5. What flavour is ouzo spirit? **Aniseed**

6. Who created the priest detective Father Brown? **G K Chesterton**

7. What colour connects a medal, flowery prose passages and an imperial butterfly? **Purple**

8. Harry, Albert, Sam and Jack founded and operated which film studios? **Warner Brothers**

9. What, apart from boards to clean knives on, were knifeboards? **Seats (on trams etc.)**

10. Which popular TV series sprang out of a series called *Police Surgeon*? ***The Avengers***

11. Who would talk about the K-T boundary? Cartographers, geologists or trawler fishermen? **Geologists**

12. Who had No 1 hits with *Is There Something I Should Know?* and *The Reflex*? **Duran Duran**

13. Which German rocket scientist was the brains behind the US space programme? **Werner Von Braun**

14. Which part of Peter Pan was kept in a drawer in the Darling household? **His shadow**

15. Who starred with his wife in the films *The Long Hot Summer*, *Rally Round the Flag Boys* and *Mr and Mrs Bridge*? **Paul Newman**

16. What's the range of the pH scale? Is it 1 to 109, 1 to 27 or 0 to 14? **0 to 14**

17. Which club did footballer Mark Hughes join in 1995? **Chelsea**

18. In a Shakespeare play, which character tamed the shrew, Katharina? **Petruchio**

19. Which US poet was indicted for treason during World War 2 and committed to a mental hospital? **Ezra Pound**

20. What is the name of the Indian savoury consisting of spiced meat or vegetables in a triangular pastry case? **Samosa**

Quiz 3

1. Hitler's personal secretary, a powerful man, disappeared at the end of World War 2. Who was he? **Martin Bormann**

2. Which character has been played in films by Walter Huston, Ray Milland, Ray Walston, Claude Rains, Vincent Price and Donald Pleasence? **The Devil**

3. Ambassadors to Britain are officially credited to which court? **The Court of St James**

4. Which coloured US soldier was chairman of the Joint Chiefs of Staff during the Gulf War? **Colin Powell**

5. In which city was the 1995 Rugby Union World Cup Final played? **Johannesburg**

6. In Northern Italy, what is the Mirror of Diana? **A lake (Nemi)**

7. Who wrote the poem *Four Quartets*, published in its entirety in 1944? **T S Eliot**

8. To whom does the warning 'caveat emptor' apply? **The buyer**

9. Which 1976 TV series was based on the true story of Rosa Lewis and the Cavendish Hotel? ***The Duchess of Duke Street***

10. Which mice are proverbially poor? **Church mice**

11. Who had Top Ten hits with *Got To Have Your Love* and *Take Your Time*? **Mantronix**

12. Which Steinbeck novel features George and Lennie? ***Of Mice and Men***

13. A ring worn on which finger indicates a masterful spirit? **Little finger**

14. True or false: there is a constellation called The Whale? **True**

15. Who is the best friend of Yogi Bear? **Boo-Boo**

16. What is the Russian for "speaking aloud"? **Glasnost**

17. Which Shakespeare play begins with these words? "In sooth, I know not why I am so sad: It wearies me; you say it wearies you . . ." ***The Merchant of Venice***

18. Which magazine, the most widely read in the world, was conceived by Dewitt Wallace and first published in 1922? ***Reader's Digest***

19. Whose Top Ten hits included *The Look*, *Joyride* and *Almost Unreal*? **Roxette's**

20. Who wrote the play *The School For Scandal*? **Sheridan**

Quiz 4

1. Who played Cliff Barnes in the TV series *Dallas*? **Ken Kercheval**

2. Who wrote the opera from which the melody known as *Here Comes the Bride* comes? **Wagner**

3. Which part of the body is affected by thlipsis: the vocal cords, the blood vessels or the joints? **The blood vessels**

4. Crosby airport is near which English city? **Carlisle**

5. What was Paul Revere's occupation? Was he the owner of a livery stable, a silversmith or a doctor? **A silversmith**

6. Which trilogy of Time Travel films was directed by Robert Zemeckis? ***Back To The Future***

7. James Figg and Jack Broughton were champions of England in which sport? **Boxing**

8. On TV, at which hospital did Dr Kildare work? **Blair Hospital**

9. What is a poniard? Is it an old coin, a dagger or a sailing ship? **A dagger**

10. True or false: oxygen makes up 30% of our atmosphere? **False (It is about 21%.)**

11. What is the heraldic emblem of Scotland? **The thistle**

12. What proportion of a person's produce was a tithe? **One tenth**

13. Who played Batman in the film *Batman Forever*? **Val Kilmer**

14. What is a true sponge? **An animal skeleton**

15. Do Waterways Airways operate in Canada, Australia or New Zealand? **New Zealand**

16. How many of our moons would equal our earth in size? **80**

17. Which branch of mathematics is called the Cossic Art? Is it Trigonometry, Calculus or Algebra? **Algebra**

18. To what use is a digitorium put? Is it to strengthen the fingers, to help cut your fingernails or to display rings in a jeweller's window? **To strengthen the fingers**

19. Whose Top Ten hits include *Be Quick or Be Dead*, *Holy Smoke* and *Infinite Dreams*? **Iron Maiden's**

20. Which one word means a unit of atmospheric pressure, a straight stripe or to obstruct or exclude? **Bar**

Quiz 5

1. Yuanjing was the first what to be bred by artificial insemination: panda, camel or tiger? **Panda**

2. Crocetti and Levitch made 16 films together from 1949 to 1956. Under what names? **Martin & Lewis**

3. In *Coronation Street*, how did Ken Barlow's second wife, Janet, die? **She committed suicide**

4. What does a pantophagist eat? **Anything**

5. Which creatures are bred by a sericulturist? **Silkworms**

6. True or false: there are 15 scales of hardness on the Mohs' scale? **False (There are 10.)**

7. Is a gallivat a pleasure-seeker, a boat or an insect? **A boat**

8. Followers of the Franciscan Friar, Duns Scotus, inspired which common word? **Dunce**

9. In *Peter and the Wolf*, which instruments represent Peter? **Violins**

10. Whose Top Ten hits included *Slave To Love*, *This Is Tomorrow* and *A Hard Rain's Gonna Fall*? **Bryan Ferry's**

11. Reg Cox was found dead in the first episode of which soap in 1985? ***Eastenders***

12. Which John Osborne play featured the seedy music hall comedian Archie Rice? ***The Entertainer***

13. What sort of cross was the German decoration The Iron Cross? **Maltese Cross**

14. In Hindu mythology, Nandini was the symbol of fertility. Was Nandini a cow, a rabbit or a turtle? **Cow**

15. In which dangerous activity is a paravane used? **Mine-sweeping**

16. Which colour is common to the flags of Venezuela, Belgium and Sweden? **Yellow**

17. Which king in Shakespeare died by having poison poured into his ear? **Hamlet – Hamlet's father**

18. Which Mel Brooks film was a spoof of Hitchcock's films? ***High Anxiety***

19. Which ruined abbey stands on the banks of the River Skell next to Studley Royal near Ripon? **Fountains Abbey**

20. Which novel by Aldous Huxley is set in the seventh century AF? ***Brave New World***

Quiz 6

1. Who was Brian Clough's assistant manager at Derby County and Notts Forest? **Peter Taylor**

2. True or false: *Beta Vulgaris* is the Latin name for sugar beet? **True**

3. What is prase? **A type of quartz**

4. If you are scorbutic, what disease are you suffering from? **Scurvy**

5. Which historic event was described by a main participant as "the nearest run thing you ever saw in your life"? **Battle of Waterloo**

6. Which was London's first railway terminus? **Euston Station**

7. Which international actress starred in *Lassie Come Home* and *Courage of Lassie*? **Elizabeth Taylor**

8. How much was a 1950 pound worth in 1990? Was it 20p, 15p or 10p? **15p**

9. Black Diamond could be seen on US nickels from 1913 to 1938. What was Black Diamond? **A bison**

10. Which king was the Rye House Plot of 1683 aiming to assassinate? **Charles II**

11. When were postcodes introduced in the UK? Was it 1968, 1970 or 1972? **1968**

12. Daphne Clarke, Jane Harris and Shane Ramsay were characters in which TV soap? ***Neighbours***

13. Who, in Robin Hood's gang, was the son of a miller? **Much**

14. Which workers belong to UCATT? **Building workers**

15. Who composed the music for the opera *Ivanhoe* in 1890? **Sir Arthur Sullivan**

16. As what did Joseph Grimaldi achieve everlasting fame? **A clown**

17. Who had Top Ten hits with *Delta Lady* and *Up Where We Belong*? **Joe Cocker**

18. True or false: Garibaldi led the expedition of the Thousand in 1850? **False (1860)**

19. What do kleptomaniacs keep doing? **Stealing**

20. Who wrote the words and music for the musical *Fings Ain't Wot They Used To Be*? **Lionel Bart**

Quiz 7

1. What is French White? **Talcum powder**
2. Which seaside resort was advertised as "so bracing"? **Skegness**
3. Can a scissile object be stretched, cut or easily bent? **Cut**
4. Who wrote *How the Camel Got His Hump* and *How the Leopard Got His Spots*? **Rudyard Kipling**
5. Who played the gunfighter in *Shane* and Attila the Hun in *Sign of the Pagan*? **Jack Palance**
6. Who played Oliver in the TV series *Oliver's Travels*? **Alan Bates**
7. In which sport was Vera Caslavska a World and Olympic Champion? **Gymnastics**
8. In Morse Code, what letter is represented by three dots and a dash? **V**
9. Who launched the C5, an electric three wheeled vehicle, in 1985? **Clive Sinclair**
10. What name is given to the method of joining two metals by melting an alloy at a joint at a higher temperature than soldering? **Brazing**
11. What was Agatha Christie's maiden name? Was it Mallowan, Mitchell or Miller? **Miller**
12. Who played Emma Harte and aged from 15 to 80 in *A Woman of Substance*? **Jenny Seagrove**
13. In which country was Antonio Salazar dictator for many years? **Portugal**

14. True or false: *brassica rapa* is the Latin name for the turnip? **True**

15. Which road along the north bank of the Thames leads from Westminster to Blackfriars? **The Embankment**

16. Which part of the body is beaten in bastinado? **Soles of the feet**

17. Which is the slowest swimming stroke? **Breast stroke**

18. Which game, developed at Public Schools, is played by hitting a small, hard ball at the wall by players wearing padded gloves? **Fives**

19. Who directed the films *Billy Liar*, *Marathon Man* and *Midnight Cowboy*? **John Schlesinger**

20. In which UK city did de Lorean set up a sports car factory in 1978? **Belfast**

Quiz 8

1. Which one word means an insect, an error in a computing program and a listening device? **Bug**

2. Who is the wife of bandleader Johnny Dankworth? **Cleo Laine**

3. What does E stand for in E-Numbers? **European**

4. Whom did Douglas Hurd succeed as Foreign Secretary? **John Major**

5. What is the name of the US anti-terrorist force based at Fort Bragg? **Delta Force**

6. Which king of England wrote *A Counterblast To Tobacco*? **James I**

7. Who played Selwyn Froggatt on TV? **Bill Maynard**

8. Which part of the body do phrenologists study? **The skull**

9. Who had a No 1 in 1992 with *Ebenezer Goode*? **The Shamen**

10. True or false: Prokofiev wrote an opera called *The Love For Three Apples*? **False (It was *The Love For Three Oranges*.)**

11. In which Shakespeare play do Leontes and Hermione, King and Queen of Sicilia, appear? ***The Winter's Tale***

12. In sport, what is the popular name for the Dwight Davis International Bowl? **Davis Cup**

13. An excess of bile pigment in the bloodstream causes what? **Jaundice**

14. Who played Elizabeth I in the second *Blackadder* series? **Miranda Richardson**

15. From which building was WPC Yvonne Fletcher shot and murdered? **Libyan Embassy**

16. What was the sequel to *Alice's Adventures in Wonderland*? ***Through the Looking-Glass***

17. What is the mathematical term for a six-sided solid whose faces are all rectangles (eg a brick)? **A cuboid**

18. Orlando Gibbons was famous as what? **He was a keyboard player**

19. Who appeared in all three of the following films: *Chariots of Fire*, *Empire of the Sun* and *The Whistle Blower*? **Nigel Havers**

20. From the flowers of which fruit is the oil neroli distilled? Is it orange, avocado or olive? **Orange**

Quiz 9

1. What is the name of the children's game played on the fingers with looped string? **Cat's Cradle**

2. FIDE is the governing body of which game? **Chess**

3. Who had Top Ten hits with *Lullaby*, *High* and *The Love Cats*? **The Cure**

4. What is a jargonelle? Is it a type of language, a pear or a songbird? **Pear**

5. What are the dark, lowland plains on the moon called? **Maria (Seas)**

6. True or false: the Indianapolis 500 was first held in 1931? **False (1911)**

7. In which English city is Lime Street Station? **Liverpool**

8. What is Princess Margaret's middle name? **Rose**

9. In Greek mythology, what form did the monster Charybdis take? **Whirlpool**

10. Who appeared in the films *Wuthering Heights*, *Flash Gordon* and *The Rocketeer*? **Timothy Dalton**

11. What would you do with a kaki? Wear it, eat it or sleep on it? **Eat it (fruit)**

12. Of which country was Christina queen from 1632 to 1654, until forced to abdicate? **Sweden**

13. What everyday articles are decorated with the King's Pattern? **Cutlery**

14. Who had Top Ten hits with *I'm Every Woman* and *Ain't Nobody*? **Chaka Khan**

15. Who was Mary Arden's famous son? **William Shakespeare**

16. Which Dorset fishing town became a centre for fossil hunters from 1811? **Lyme Regis**

17. In geometry, what is a line joining any two points on a curve called? **Chord**

18. Which Frenchman was European Footballer of the Year from 1983 to 1985? **Michel Platini**

19. Which android was played on TV by Matt Frewer? ***Max Headroom***

20. What is the common name for chorea, a disease of the nervous system which causes involuntary movements? **St Vitus' Dance**

Quiz 10

1. Jai Alai is another name for which ball game? **Pelota**

2. True or false: Colonel Thomas Pride expelled 140 MPs from the House of Commons in 1648? **True**

3. Which daily newspaper is printed on pink paper? ***The Financial Times***

4. What is sold in a white sale? **Household linen**

5. Trim, Meg, Nap and Nip have each been one half of duos that have won which competition? ***One Man and His Dog***

6. Which TV series featured the portly cooking detective Henry Crabbe? ***Pie In the Sky***

7. What does an aurologist study? **Diseases of the ear**

8. Which 1993 film produced both Best Actress and Best Supporting Actress Oscars? ***The Piano***

9. H W Fowler produced a book of guidelines to what in 1926? **Correct English**

10. Who, allegedly, told Shakespeare to write *The Merry Wives of Windsor*? **Elizabeth I**

11. In the USA, which battle is remembered in April on Patriots' Day? **Lexington**

12. Who had Top Ten hits with *Come Back and Stay*, *Every Time You Go Away* and *Senza Una Donna*? **Paul Young**

13. What is a gytrash? Is it a falcon, a ghost or a type of moulding? **A ghost**

14. In which county is Charterhouse Public School? Is it Berkshire, Buckinghamshire or Surrey? **Surrey**

15. True or false: the word grabble means to grope or feel about for? **True**

16. Which sport, played on a court 32 feet by 21 feet in Britain, is governed by the IRF? **Racketball**

17. Who coined the phrase 'gnomes of Zurich' when referring to international financiers? **Harold Wilson**

18. True or false: Edward I was the eldest son of Henry II? **False (Son of Henry III.)**

19. Which one word means a piece of business, a plank of fir or pine and to give out cards? **Deal**

20. Whose Top Ten hits include *Church of the Poison Mind*, *Victims* and *Move Away*? **Culture Club**

Quiz 11

1. What colour is traditionally associated with Roman emperors? **Purple**

2. What name is given to the flap of cartilage which prevents food from entering your windpipe? **Epiglottis**

3. What sort of fruit is a Laxton Superb? Is it an apple, a strawberry or a plum? **Apple**

4. Under what name did Lord Tweedsmuir write several novels? **John Buchan**

5. What is the more common name for grape-sugar? Is it gluten, glucose or lactose? **Glucose**

6. What is a labret? Is it the front part of an insect's head, an ornament inserted through the lip, or culpable negligence in legal matters? **A lip ornament**

7. Areas of equal . . . (what?) are connected by a line called an isohyet on a map? **Rainfall**

8. In which American state are the towns of Anaconda and Moscow and the Salmon River? **Idaho**

9. In which sport is there competition for the America's Cup? **Yachting**

10. Which British island, about 80 feet across, is in the Atlantic, 230 miles west of the Hebrides? **Rockall**

11. What was supposed to flow in the veins of the Greek gods? **Ichor**

12. In which film did POWs use a vaulting horse to disguise the digging of an escape tunnel? ***The Wooden Horse***

13. Which drink was advertised by Leonard Rossiter and Joan Collins? **Cinzano**

14. What was the name of the aging rock band in the 1987 TV series *Tutti Frutti*? **The Majestics**

15. Which straits separate Sri Lanka from India? Is it the Straits of Jaffna, the Comorin Straits or the Palk Straits? **Palk Straits**

16. True or false: Glyndebourne Opera House is in East Sussex? **True**

17. Who designed the tapestry which hangs behind the altar in Coventry cathedral? **Graham Sutherland**

18. Which animal gives us nutria fur? Is it the capybara, coypu or wolverine? **Coypu**

19. Who said: "It's a funny old world – a man's lucky if he gets out of it alive."? **W C Fields**

20. What is the collective word for a group of foxes? **Skulk**

Quiz 12

1. In which novel did Michael Henchard sell his wife for 5 guineas? ***The Mayor of Casterbridge***

2. For which English king did Handel compose his *Water Music*? **George I**

3. What colour was Alexandre Dumas' tulip? **Black**

4. What is the square root of 729? **27**

5. On what material does a topiarist work? **Hedges and shrubs**

6. In which club did Arthur and Terry drink in the TV series *Minder*? **The Winchester**

7. Which famous adventure story was originally titled *The Sea Cook*? ***Treasure Island***

8. Mainly which creatures belong to the order *arachnida*? **Spiders**

9. From which country did the Bashi Bazouks come? Was it Turkey, Morocco or Persia? **Turkey**

10. Which fruit did Columbus discover on Guadeloupe in 1493? Was it the pineapple, banana or the melon? **Pineapple**

11. Who played the named character in these films? *Darby's Rangers*, *Mister Buddwing* and *Marlowe*? **James Garner**

12. True or false: there is actually a country named Cape Verde? **True**

13. Which Christian name derives from the Gaelic for 'handsome'? **Kenneth**

14. From which affliction did the patient Job suffer in the Bible? Was it leprosy, boils or blindness? **Boils**

15. What is the family name of the Dukes of Wellington? **Wellesley**

16. In which city were the 1896 Olympic Games held? **Athens**

17. What is the sport for which Sabina Park is famous? **Cricket**

18. In *Macbeth*, who was Banquo's son? Was it Fleance, Donalbain or Seyton? **Fleance**

19. Who had a hit in 1972 with *Sylvia's Mother*? **Doctor Hook**

20. Which English football club play at Roots Hall? **Southend United**

Quiz 13

1. In which film did Lee Marvin throw boiling coffee in Gloria Grahame's face? ***The Big Heat***

2. Which gas is manufactured by the Haber Process? Is it ammonia, chlorine or helium? **Ammonia**

3. Who owned the High Chaparral ranch? **John Cannon**

4. Two musical notes have no actual flats. Name one. **C or F**

5. If a woman is nubile, what does that mean? **Marrigeable**

6. What is an odalisque? Is it a room in a mosque, a female slave or a stone in Stonehenge? **Female slave**

7. What does a mycologist study? Is it mosses, fungi or muscles? **Fungi**

8. True or false: Henry Patrick McCarty was Billy the Kid's real name? **True**

9. Who said: "The great masses of the people will more easily fall victim to a big lie than to a small one."? **Hitler**

10. Who had Top Ten hits in the 1980s with *Run To the Hills*, *Can I Play With Madness* and *The Evil That Men Do*? **Iron Maiden**

11. Who sailed away to die on HMS *Bellerophon*? **Napoleon**

12. What was the actual practical purpose of a gargoyle? **Water spout**

13. What finally stood in for Roy Hattersley when he couldn't appear on *Have I Got News For You* on TV? **A tub of lard**

14. What were once called 'love apples'? **Tomatoes**

15. What is tilth? Is it cultivation, a type of rock, or a mark placed over 'n' in some Spanish words? **Cultivation**

16. What originally gave foolscap paper its name? **The watermark**

17. In which sport is there something named after Ulrich Salchow? **Ice skating**

18. In a famous Dickens novel, who was helped financially by Abel Magwitch? **Pip**

19. After which famous engineer is the university at Uxbridge named? **Brunel**

20. If ursine is bearlike and equine horselike, what is vulpine? **Foxlike**

Quiz 14

1. The Bible says 'a fool returneth to his folly as a dog returneth to his . . . (what?)'? **Vomit**

2. What is a bugloss? Is it a plant, a snake or a songbird? **Plant (herb)**

3. Who had Top Ten hits with *What Can You Do For Me?*, *Something Good* and *Believe In Me*? **Utah Saints**

4. Which type of art was founded by Jasper Johns? **Pop Art**

5. The Gulf of Sidra is off the coast of which African country? **Libya**

6. Who is the Countess of Snowdon? **Princess Margaret**

7. Which sport is thought to have originated at Kingston, Ontario, in 1855? **Ice Hockey**

8. In the film *Howard – A New Kind of Hero*, what was Howard? **A duck**

9. From which story does this line come? "Who will change old lamps for new, new lamps for old?" ***Aladdin***

10. Which king allegedly said on his deathbed: "Let not poor Nelly starve."? **Charles II**

11. Who invented the flying shuttle in weaving? **John Kay**

12. True or false: Seattle is in the state of Philadelphia? **False (Washington)**

13. Who opened a boutique called *Bazaar* in 1957? **Mary Quant**

14. What is the collective name for Lady Day, Midsummer Day, Michaelmas Day and Christmas Day? **Quarter Days**

15. Brigadier Lethbridge-Stewart appeared in many episodes of which TV series? ***Dr Who***

16. *Nemo me impune lacessit* is the motto of which Scottish Order of Knighthood? **The Order of theThistle**

17. The character Paul Kersey appears in which series of Michael Winner films? ***Death Wish***

18. Who wrote "To err is human, to forgive divine"? Donne, Pope or Milton? **Pope**

19. Which one word means a wading bird, a pole with a foot rest and a support for raising a building above ground level? **Stilt**

20. Who plays Frasier Crane in *Cheers* and *Frasier*? **Kelsey Grammer**

Quiz 15

1. In sport, what can be 106cm, 91cm or 84cm in height? **Hurdles**

2. Where in the British Isles are Onchan Head, Port Soderick and Union Mills? **Isle of Man**

3. Hides, hundreds and wapentakes were all what? **Areas of land**

4. Where were the 1920 Olympics held? **Antwerp (Belgium)**

5. Who had Top Ten hits with *The Size of a Cow* and *Welcome to the Cheap Seats*? **Wonder Stuff**

6. Who was trapped by the Tar Baby and then thrown into a brier patch? **Brer Rabbit**

7. In which art form is *contrapposto* used? **Sculpture**

8. True or false: Leopold Stokowski was born in Britain? **True**

9. In what year was the Russian Revolution? **1917**

10. What is a sidewinder? **A rattlesnake**

11. Who had Top Ten hits with *Do I Do*, *Lately* and *I Wish*? **Stevie Wonder**

12. Which bird did Wordsworth describe as "Ethereal minstrel! pilgrim of the sky!"? **Skylark**

13. American meat inspector Samuel Wilson is thought to have been the inspiration for which personification? **Uncle Sam**

14. Where in London is Winfield House, The Holme and The Broad Walk? **Regent's Park**

15. Is a tarpon a fish, a piglike animal or an old weapon? **Fish**

16. Which country had a campaign called Hundred Flowers? India, Japan or China? **China**

17. Who played Rita's tutor in the film *Educating Rita*? **Michael Caine**

18. Which poet developed 'sprung rhythm'? **Gerard Manley Hopkins**

19. Who was Queen Victoria's last Prime Minister? Was it Gladstone, Lord Rosebery or the Marquis of Salisbury? **Marquis of Salisbury**

20. In which Shakespeare play do suitors have to choose one of three caskets? ***The Merchant of Venice***

Quiz 16

1. Devil's apron and purple laver are types of what? **Seaweed**

2. Who was the father of David? Was it Zachariah, Absalom or Jesse? **Jesse**

3. Under what nickname did Albert de Salvo become infamous? ***The Boston Strangler***

4. True or false: vernal means easily bribed? **False (It means to do with spring.)**

5. What is the name of the metal discs in the rim of a tambourine? Are they pings, tinklers or jingles? **Jingles**

6. In Gaelic legend, who had a dog called Bran? **Fingal**

7. Who played Eliza Doolittle in the film *My Fair Lady*? **Audrey Hepburn**

8. What are ossicles and osselets? **Bones**

9. Soling, Star and Finn are categories in which sport? **Yachting**

10. Which device allows a car's driving wheels to turn at different speeds when cornering? **Differential**

11. Which large object was discovered by Clyde Tombaugh in 1930? **Pluto**

12. Disc jockey Alan Freed popularised and helped to name which type of music from 1951? **Rock 'n Roll**

13. In poker, which is the best hand of these: flush, run (straight) or three of a kind? **Flush**

14. Which King of England's mother and son were both beheaded? **James I's**

15. To what is the French word 'chambré' applied? **Wine**

16. True or false: Dashiel Hammett created the detective Philip Marlowe? **False (Raymond Chandler did.)**

17. To what does the adjective 'Pontic' apply? **The Black Sea**

18. What term is used to measure the fineness of yarns? **Denier**

19. Which ruler led the 7th and 8th Crusades: Richard I, Louis IX or Frederick II? **Louis IX**

20. What is 2nd February called in the USA? **Ground-hog Day**

Quiz 17

1. What does the abbreviation GDP stand for?
Gross Domestic Product

2. Who played the named character in these films: *Kitty Foyle*, *Roxie Hart* and *Magnificent Doll*?
Ginger Rogers

3. Which calendar did Britain adopt in 1752?
Gregorian

4. Who presented the TV show *Sweethearts* in 1987?
Larry Grayson

5. After which Norse goddess is Friday named?
Frigga or Freya

6. In 1993, which country ranked third in terms of population? Was it India, USA or Indonesia?
USA

7. Which of the Seven Wonders of the World was constructed by the sculptor Phidias about 430 BC?
Statue of Zeus

8. Who is the patron saint of singers? Is it Gregory, Vitus or Andrew? **St Gregory**

9. Which video-cassette system, introduced in the 1970s, couldn't compete with VHS and disappeared? **Betamax**

10. What is the Greek equivalent of the Roman deity Pax? **Irene**

11. Who had a No 1 with *Reet Petite* almost 30 years after he'd first had it in the Top Ten? **Jackie Wilson**

12. True or false: the Egyptian god Osiris was the son of Nut? **True**

13. Of which country was Achmed Sukarno President from 1945 to 1962? **Indonesia**

14. Which German physicist formulated the quantum theory? **Max Planck**

15. What is pott? Is it a paper size, re-fired pottery or a consultation? **Paper size**

16. In what field did Norman Parkinson make his name? **Photography**

17. What instrument was played by jazz musician John Coltrane? **Saxophone**

18. Which novel by Michael Crichton was No 1 bestseller paperback in 1993? ***Jurassic Park***

19. In which sport did Irina Rodnina win 23 World, Olympic and European gold medals? **Ice skating**

20. Who won Best Actress Oscar for her role in *Coming Home* (1978)? **Jane Fonda**

Quiz 18

1. Which pop group featured in the film *The Great Rock 'n Roll Swindle*? **The Sex Pistols**

2. Which film star's real name was Emmanuel Goldenberg? **Edward G Robinson's**

3. Which was the world's first commercial jet aircraft? ***The Comet***

4. True or false: you can legally shoot pheasant in September? **False (season starts *October 1st*)**

5. In the Wild West, what did the Indians call whiskey? **Firewater**

6. Who was the villain in *Wacky Races*? **Dick Dastardly**

7. In which county is the leisure park Alton Towers? **Derbyshire**

8. Where are the heads of four former US Presidents carved in stone? **Mount Rushmore**

9. Which star did the killing in the film *Dial M For Murder*? **Grace Kelly**

10. By what name in the 1940s and 1950s was Charles Hill known on the radio? **The Radio Doctor**

11. Which animals are affected by the disease vives? **Horses**

12. What connects Da Vinci's *Statue of a Horse*, Coleridge's *Kubla Khan* and Schubert's *8th Symphony*? **All unfinished**

13. Which song did Doris Day sing in three different films? ***Que Sera Sera***

14. In Wales, what is Cader Idris? **Mountain range**

15. With which sport was Neville Cardus associated? **Cricket**

16. Which notorious twosome were killed in an ambush near Arcadia, Louisiana, on 23rd May 1934? **Bonnie and Clyde**

17. Who had Top Ten hits with *Black Knight* and *Strange Kind of Woman*? **Deep Purple**

18. Who owned, edited and contributed to the magazine *Household Words*? **Charles Dickens**

19. In which year was the length of the marathon fixed at 26 miles 385 yards? **1908**

20. True or false: A A Milne's son was called Christopher Robin? **True**

Quiz 19

1. Who said: "You Americans keep saying that Cuba is 90 miles from the US. I say that the US is 90 miles from Cuba, and for us that is worse."? **Fidel Castro**

2. What nickname was given in the 1950s to suede shoes with rubber or crepe soles? **Brothel Creepers**

3. Before Nigel Mansell, who was the last Briton to win the British Grand Prix – in 1981? **John Watson**

4. In which G B Shaw play, set in America during the War Of Independence, is a smuggler saved from execution by a minister? ***The Devil's Disciple***

5. What was the name of David Low's pompous, fat, bald, retired army officer, opposed to any change? **Colonel Blimp**

6. At sea, at a height cf 500 feet above sea level, how far would you be able to see? **29 to 30 miles**

7. Which word, derived from the French, means the unravelling, or final solution, of a plot? **Dénouement**

8. Who played the lead in the film *The Stone Killer*?
Charles Bronson

9. Which is the highest Order of Chivalry in Britain?
Order of the Garter

10. Which TV series had characters called Jack Rolfe, Ken Masters, Claude du Pont and Charles Frere?
Howard's Way

11. Of which musical instrument is this a description? "Valveless brass or copper instrument of treble pitch, with wide tube of conical bore, a moderate sized bell, and cup-shaped mouthpiece." **Bugle**

12. Which successful movie star was nicknamed Greer Garson in furs? **Lassie**

13. In which event did Steve Backley hold the World record? **Javelin**

14. Which newsreader was a regular panellist on *Face the Music*? **Richard Baker**

15. Existing from 1875 to 1958, what was the Carla Rosa? **An opera company**

16. True or false: Reparata and the Delrons never had a Top Ten hit in the UK? **True**

17. What would a tinchel of men be doing? **Hunting**

18. Which Cumbrian town is noted for an annual horse fair? **Appleby**

19. Who had Top Ten hits with *Hong Kong Garden* and *Dear Prudence*? **Siouxsie and the Banshees**

20. Who wrote: "All women become like their mothers. That is their tragedy. No man does. That is his."?
Oscar Wilde

Quiz 20

1. In which British city are the Ferens Art Gallery, Wilberforce House and the Town Docks Museum? **Hull**

2. In which film did cop Harrison Ford hide out on an Amish farm? ***Witness***

3. Leap of the Hare, Tree Climber, Spinning Top and Chasing the Sparrow are all described in detail in which book? ***Kama Sutra***

4. In which American state is Monument valley? **Arizona**

5. Kim Campbell became the first woman Prime Minister of which country in 1993? **Canada**

6. The specialist magazine *Zymurgy* deals with brewing, sci-fi or health care? **Brewing**

7. Who composed the music for the musicals *Strike Up the Band*, *Lady Be Good* and *Girl Crazy*? **George Gershwin**

8. Who gave the agents their orders in *The Man From UNCLE*? **Mr Waverly**

9. Who wrote the plays *The Dwarfs*, *The Homecoming* and *Old Times*? **Harold Pinter**

10. The Blue Cross Charity, founded in 1897, brings aid to what? **Animals**

11. Which is England's oldest daily newspaper? ***The Times***

12. True or false: Thomas Arnold was a famous headmaster of Harrow school? **False (Rugby school)**

13. What is an anaconda? **A snake**

14. According to the song, on which town's bridge does everybody dance? **Avignon**

15. Children's Temperance Societies began in 1850 and were called what? **Band of Hope**

16. Who had Top Ten hits with *Sowing the Seeds of Love* and *Everybody Wants To Rule the World*? **Tears For Fears**

17. Words beginning 'litho' generally have to do with what? **Stone**

18. Who wrote *The Dynasts*, a work that deals with the war with Napoleon? **Thomas Hardy**

19. What name is given to the list of characters in a play? **Dramatis Personae**

20. Who played the lead in the films *Private's Progress*, *Brothers In Law* and *Lucky Jim*? **Ian Carmichael**

Quiz 21

1. For what purpose would tree-calf be used? **For book binding**

2. Who was left on a desert island in TV's *Girl Friday*? **Joanna Lumley**

3. What word describes a person who gains illegal access to computers? **Hacker**

4. True or false: a papillon is a breed of dog. **True**

5. What happened off the Grand Banks of Newfoundland on 14th April, 1912? **The *Titanic* sank.**

6. Who writes and sends encyclical letters? **The Pope**

7. Which Prime Minister's second term of office included the General Strike, the grant of pensions for widows and complete adult suffrage? **Stanley Baldwin's**

8. Which stretch of water separates Denmark from Norway? **Skagerrak**

9. Who was offered a million dollars to sleep with Robert Redford in the film *Indecent Proposal*? **Demi Moore**

10. Where do plants known as hydrophytes live? **In water**

11. Which philosophy lecturer wrote *The Second Sex* and *The Mandarins*? **Simone de Beauvoir**

12. What is coppicing? **Pruning trees**

13. From which planet does Mork come? **Ork**

14. Which people used the quipu (knotted cords) for calculation? Was it the Mayas, the Aztecs or the Incas? **Incas**

15. In Chinese history, who was Pu Yi? **The Last Emperor**

16. Who played Henry VIII in the TV series *The Six Wives of Henry VIII*? **Keith Michell**

17. Whose Top Ten hits included *Love To Hate You*, *Breath of Life* and *Run To the Sun*? **Erasure**

18. What is the unit of currency in Ecuador? **Sucre**

19. In which country was the Battle of Pinkie fought in 1547? **Scotland**

20. True or false: the fruit of the baobab tree is called monkey bread? **True**

Quiz 22

1. From whom did Shylock wish to take his pound of flesh? **Antonio**

2. George Galvin was a famous music-hall entertainer under which name? **Dan Leno**

3. The Jewish festival Purim celebrates the story of which woman in the Bible? **Esther**

4. What colour eggs are the Chinese symbol of luck and new life? **Red**

5. In mythology, who was the mother of Hector? **Hecuba**

6. Which once common disease was also known as The White Death? **Tuberculosis**

7. Spell Humorous. **Humorous**

8. True or false: Salisbury Crags are in Edinburgh? **True**

9. In which African country do the Hausa people live? **Nigeria**

10. Who succeeded U Thant as Secretary General of the UN? **Kurt Waldheim**

11. Which bone is between your femur and your tibia? **Patella**

12. Under what name did Nathan Birnbaum become famous? **George Burns**

13. Of what do fennel leaves taste? Is it onion, pepper or aniseed? **Aniseed**

14. Who was Desmond Lynam's co-presenter on the first series of *How Do They Do That*? **Jennie Hull**

15. Which French soldier's name became the word for a strict disciplinarian? **(Jean) Martinet**

16. How many islands make up the Maldives? Is it (roughly) 850, 1200 or 1500? **1200 (1196)**

17. Which film ends like this? Mounted Soldier (Charlton Heston) reaches out to a little girl and says: "Here, take my hand"? ***55 Days at Peking***

18. Which singer had Top Ten hits in the1980s with *Games Without Frontiers* and *Sledgehammer*? **Peter Gabriel**

19. In which constellation is the star Betelgeuse? **Orion**

20. Who was the Norse god of poetry? Was it Bragi, Balder or Hoder? **Bragi**

Quiz 23

1. How many players are there in a baseball team? **Nine**

2. What was the name of the Hoover Dam on the Colorado River from 1933 to 1947? **Boulder Dam**

3. How long is a Gunter's chain? Is it 66 feet, 100 feet or 144 feet? **66 feet**

4. True or false: Athos, Porthos and Aramis all appear in the novel *Vicomte de Bragelonne*? **True**

5. What was to be suppressed by 'comstockery'? **Corrupting literature**

6. Russian, Fleury, Tau and Papal are all types of what? **Crosses**

7. Who said: "I'll bet your father spent the first year of your life throwing rocks at the stork."? **Groucho Marx**

8. Who was the guzzling and greedy giant created by Rabelais? **Gargantua**

9. Which natural feature has been nicknamed The Lamp of Phoebus? **The sun**

10. Which Quaker founded the city of Philadelphia? **William Penn**

11. In which film, based on Conrad's *Heart of Darkness*, did Martin Sheen seek Marlon Brando? ***Apocalypse Now***

12. Who defined the Four Freedoms in 1941? **Franklin D Roosevelt**

13. Which sport is now believed to be the origin of the expression 'The Real McCoy'? **Boxing**

14. Which bird is nicknamed Pharaoh's Chicken? **(Egyptian) Vulture**

15. Which vocal group comprised Cass, Michelle, John and Denny? **The Mamas and The Papas**

16. Which helpful organisation was founded by the Rev Chad Varah in 1953? **Samaritans**

17. What name was and is used by American Black Nationalists for negroes who are too subservient to white people? **Uncle Tom**

18. What was the name of the cook in TV's *Upstairs Downstairs*? **Mrs Bridges**

19. Whom does Viola love in *Twelfth Night*? **Duke Orsino**

20. True or false: saxifrage is a small rock plant? **True**

Quiz 24

1. Who originally travelled the Via Dolorosa? **Jesus**

2. In the RAF, how many squadrons make up a wing? **Three**

3. Which part of Britain, because of local pronunciation, is sometimes called Zedland? **The West Country**

4. What instrument is played by the leader of an orchestra? **Violin**

5. Who produced an album called *An Innocent Man*? **Billy Joel**

6. Which Archbishop of Canterbury, later canonised, was said to have seized the devil's nose in a pair of red-hot tongs? **Dunstan**

7. In the nursery rhyme, who visited the person with a little nut tree? **The King of Spain's daughter**

8. Who said: "The maxim of the British people is 'Business as usual'."? **Winston Churchill**

9. What is a grackle? Is it a fish, a lizard or a bird? **Bird (Oriole)**

10. Add together Buchan's steps, Sayers' Tailors and Rome's hills. **55 (39+9+7)**

11. What was revealed by a letter to Lord Monteagle? **The Gunpowder Plot**

12. In which TV series did Richard Chamberlain play an Australian priest whose son also became a priest? ***The Thorn Birds***

13. Which slang word for prison came into use from the name of a famous gaol in Southwark in London? **Clink**

14. Which of these is NOT a member of the antelope family: impala, eland, hyrax, dik-dik? **Hyrax**

15. What kind of cross-country running involves two runners setting off early and leaving a trail for the chasing runners to follow? **Hare and Hounds**

16. True or false: the National Anthem of Portugal is *Our Fatherland*? **False (Portugal's is *The Portuguese*.)**

17. What is the name of the dinosaur monster which has appeared in many Japanese films? **Godzilla**

18. In which religion is the mystic formula Om Mani Padme Hum chanted? **Buddhism**

19. How much would you be paid if you held an honorary post? **Nothing**

20. In ancient mythology, what was a lamia? A fabulous horse, a female demon or a magic shield? **Female demon**

Quiz 25

1. In fairy folklore, what was the job of Mab? **Midwife**

2. In the Bible, what instrument did David play? **Harp**

3. In which British city was the the warning cry "Gardy Loo" used when people upstairs were emptying the slop out of the window? **Edinburgh**

4. In the TV series *Edward and Mrs Simpson*, who played Edward? **Edward Fox**

5. Which country has the motto "E Pluribus Unum" on its Great Seal? **USA**

6. What was the title of the spoof version of *The Maltese Falcon*, made in 1975 and starring George Segal as Sam Spade Jr? ***The Black Bird***

7. Which literary character rode a horse called Rosinante? **Don Quixote**

8. Under a now obsolete system, who would be granted a Ticket of Leave? **A convict (A type of parole.)**

9. What is Tiddy-oggie? Is it a Cornish pasty, a Welsh stew or a Norfolk fish pie? **Cornish pasty**

10. Who had Top Ten hits in the 1960s with *Detroit City*, *I'm Coming Home* and *Love Me Tonight*? **Tom Jones**

11. How many players did England use in the 1966 Football World Cup Finals? Was it 15, 16 or 17?
15

12. In which Commonwealth country is Waitangi Day the national day? **New Zealand**

13. True or false: Zoroastrianism is an ancient Turkish religion? **False (Persian)**

14. Who played Michael Douglas's wife in *Fatal Attraction*? **Anne Archer**

15. What name is given to foolishly extravagant or useless structures built for amusement or pride?
Follies

16. Which one word fits these definitions: a small falcon, a small horse and a pastime? **Hobby**

17. According to Revelations, what is the number of the Beast? **666**

18. On whose shoulders did the Old Man of the Sea hoist himself? **Sinbad the Sailor's**

19. Which motor racing team is named after India's sacred flower? **Lotus**

20. What are you seeking if you hold out an olive branch? **Peace**

Quiz 26

1. Where is the game shovel-board usually played?
On a ship's deck

2. For which club side did Will Carling play?
Harlequins

3. Which radioactive isotope helps to date organic materials? **Carbon-14**

4. True vellum is a writing material made from what? **Calf skin**

5. Whose Top Ten hits included *Truly*, *Say You, Say Me* and *All Night Long*? **Lionel Richie's**

6. What would an Australian aborigine point to place a curse on someone? **A bone**

7. What is called 'The Curse of Adam'? **Work**

8. Which part of the body is affected by nystagmus? **Eyes**

9. Which ship featured in the TV series *Sailing*? **HMS *Ark Royal***

10. Whom did Malcolm III succeed as King of Scotland? **Macbeth**

11. Which apostle's symbol is a sword? **St Paul's**

12. Was nim an ancient game, a halo or a martial art? **Ancient game**

13. It is easier for – what – to go through the eye of a needle than for a rich man to enter into the Kingdom of Heaven? **A camel**

14. To an airman, what was a Mae West? **Lifejacket**

15. Which one word means a 5-card card game, a light sleep and a smooth, woolly surface? **Nap**

16. Who had Top Ten hits with *Gangsters*, *Too Much Too Young* and *Nelson Mandela*? **The Specials**

17. Which piece of masonry is inscribed "Cormac McCarthy fortis me fieri fecit AD 1446"? **Blarney Stone**

18. If asses bray, monkeys chatter and snakes hiss, what do falcons do? **Chant**

19. Who played the Mother Superior in the film *Sister Act*? **Maggie Smith**

20. What do you do when you nictitate? **Wink**

Quiz 27

1. Geographically, what is an inch? **A small island**

2. Which TV serial featured the characters Gripper Stebson, Tucker Jenkins and Zammo? ***Grange Hill***

3. What is a picture or figure representing a word or phrase called? **Rebus**

4. In the film *Fantastic Voyage*, where did the craft make its voyage? **In a man's body**

5. In which sport did Britain's Yvonne MacGregor break the world record in June 1995? **Cycling**

6. In which county is Banbury? **Oxfordshire**

7. The protein casein is present in which common foodstuff? **Milk**

8. True or false: the century plant flowers only once in a hundred years? **False (Flowers and dies after 10-15 years.)**

9. What was hung around the Ancient Mariner's neck? **An albatross**

10. Who first roared into action in the MGM 1928 film *White Shadows of the South Seas*? **Leo the Lion**

11. Who played the lead in the TV series *Shogun*? **Richard Chamberlain**

12. Which one word means a string of toad's eggs, the crest of a bird and a wreath for the head? **Chaplet**

13. What is a mellophone? **A musical instrument**

14. In the Wild West, Robert, Emmett and Grattan were brothers who led a famous outlaw gang. Were they the Coles, the Youngers or the Daltons? **Daltons**

15. Which firm used Millais' famous painting *Bubbles* to advertise their product? **Pears**

16. Who had Top Ten hits with *Kayleigh*, *Lavender* and *Incommunicado*? **Marillion**

17. Who was National Hunt Champion Jockey from 1986 to 1991? **Peter Scudamore**

18. What happened to Solomon Grundy on Thursday? **He became ill**

19. Apart from the Jews, which is the longest established ethnic minority in Britain? **Chinese**

20. Chung Ling Soo, an illusionist, died in 1918 performing his most celebrated trick. What was it? **Catching the bullet**

Quiz 28

1. In Western frontier towns, what were the cemeteries usually called? **Boot Hill**

2. Boosening, immersing people in cold water, was an old method of treating what? Was it drunkenness, insanity or possession? **Insanity**

3. Which famous building was erected for the Great Exhibition of 1851? **Crystal Palace**

4. Which industry was launched by David McConnell in 1886 as a result of his selling volumes of Shakespeare door to door? **Cosmetics**

5. Which English king's son was nicknamed Prince Titi? **George II's**

6. Is a killick a stone used as an anchor, a murderous ruffian or a man's tunic? **Stone anchor**

7. What are said to be pulled out of the fire when retrieving a difficult situation for somebody? **Chestnuts**

8. Which saint was shot to death by arrows in 288 AD? **Sebastian**

9. True or false: the Tolpuddle Martyrs formed a trade union in Wiltshire? **False (It was in Dorset.)**

10. Who succeeded Robert the Bruce as King of the Scots? **David II**

11. Who owned the factory visited by Charlie Bucket in a Roald Dahl story? **Willie Wonka**

12. In which Essex town can a couple compete for a flitch as a prize for being happily married? **Dunmow**

13. For which county did Godfrey Evans play cricket? **Kent**

14. What was the name for the ancient trade route between China and the Mediterranean? **Silk Road**

15. Where did Lord Kitchener defeat the Mahdi in 1898? **Omdurman**

16. Which disease is tested for by the Schich Test? **Diphtheria**

17. With what art form was Donald McGill particularly associated? **Seaside postcards**

18. Who had Top Ten hits in the 1980s with *I'm Still Standing*, *Passengers* and *Blue Eyes*? **Elton John**

19. In which L P Hartley novel does a boy carry messages between two lovers? ***The Go-Between***

20. For what was amateur naturalist Thomas Bewick especially famous? **Engravings**

Quiz 29

1. In which US State are the Sierra Nevada mountains? **California**

2. Which island off the north coast of Devon takes its name from the Norse word for puffin? **Lundy**

3. Who played the murderer in *Kind Hearts and Coronets*? **Dennis Price**

4. Which word connects crab, mite, monkey, plant and wasp? **Spider**

5. True or false: Panay is an island in the Philippines? **True**

6. On which London street is Selfridges? **Oxford Street**

7. A strobilus is another name for a pine cone, an orchid stamen or a tulip bulb? **Pine cone**

8. Which World War 2 leader was executed and exhibited by his own people? **Mussolini**

9. What name is given to stunted and withered apples used to make rough cider? **Scrumps**

10. Shorthorn cattle were the first breed to have their own herdbook. In which county were they developed? **Durham**

11. Who was crop-dusted in the film *North By Northwest*? **Cary Grant**

12. In *Treasure Island*, who, apart from Jim Hawkins, narrates part of the story? **Dr Livesey**

13. Marcus Samuel developed Shell Oil, but what was the original family business? Was it importing tin, importing sea shells and curios, or dealing in spices? **Importing sea shells and curios**

14. Which American became World Chess Champion in 1972? **Bobby Fischer**

15. Who wrote the drama series *The Singing Detective*? **Dennis Potter**

16. What was once the traditional name for the holiday period in northern industrial towns? **Wakes Week**

17. Which team game has the positions first defence, in home and second attack? **Lacrosse**

18. Who built Wormwood Scrubs? **The convicts (Contractors built the first nine cells then the nine convicts built the next nine, and so on.)**

19. Is gneiss a type of rock, a moss or a young salmon? **Rock**

20. What was Newcastle University called when it was a college of Durham University? **King's College**

Quiz 30

1. True or false: Amy Johnson was American? **False (She was British.)**

2. Who led the Scottish forces at Bannockburn? **Robert the Bruce**

3. Who traded places with Eddie Murphy in *Trading Places*? **Dan Akroyd**

4. Which part of Britain was called Vectis by the Romans? **Isle of Wight**

5. Who narrated the 26 part TV series *The World at War*? **Laurence Olivier**

6. Tarquin the Proud was the last king of where? **Rome**

7. Which country's largest and oldest city was partly developed by a convict called Francis Greenaway? **Australia's (Sydney)**

8. On which river are the Victoria Falls? **Zambezi**

9. In Chinese cosmology, what is the contrast and complement to the Yin? **The Yang**

10. Is a saxhorn a plant, a musical instrument or an antelope? **Musical instrument**

11. Vinegar is a dilute solution of which acid? **Acetic**

12. Who, in 1907, was the first woman to receive the Order of Merit? **Florence Nightingale**

13. In which sport were Barry Briggs and Ove Fundin World Champions? **Speedway**

14. Who had Top Ten hits in the 1970s with *Come On Over To My Place*, *There Goes My First Love* and *Kissin' In the Back Row of the Movies*? **The Drifters**

15. Which idol did the Israelites make when they believed Moses would not return from Mount Sinai? **The Golden Calf**

16. What does the Dewey Decimal System classify? **(Library) Books**

17. True or false: I Ching is a Chinese method of divination? **True**

18. Who played the title role in the 1950 film *Odette*? **Anna Neagle**

19. What is sorghum? Is it a herb, a mineral oxide or a cereal crop? **Cereal crop**

20. What was Lester Piggott's first Derby winner? **Never Say Die**

Quiz 31

1. On TV, in which state was *Knots Landing*? **California**

2. Who wrote and directed the film *The Purple Rose of Cairo*? **Woody Allen**

3. With which sport is the famous expression "Go out there and win one for the Gipper" associated? **American Football**

4. True or false: the North Pole was first reached in 1912? **False (1909)**

5. Which is the City of Brotherly Love? **Philadelphia**

6. Which was Peter Beardsley's first English League Club? **Carlisle United**

7. Who was the mother of singer Lorna Luft? **Judy Garland**

8. Who danced with Gene Kelly and Debbie Reynolds in *Singing in the Rain*? **Donald O'Connor**

9. Who had Top Ten hits with *High in the Sky* and *Hello Suzie*? **Amen Corner**

10. What sort of animal was a brawn? **Wild pig or boar**

11. St Mary's, St Martin's and Tresco are main islands in which group? **Scilly Isles**

12. Which TV series featured the characters Maddie Hayes and David Addison? ***Moonlighting***

13. Is a bowyang a yokel's smock, a broad leather belt or the string workmen tied below the knee to hitch their trouser up? **String tied below the knee.**

14. Which one word means a pigsty, open or sincere, and to mark a letter to show postage has been paid? **Frank**

15. Which actor made his debut in *The Dambusters*, tried to kill James Bond, was killed by Sitting Bull's men and was eaten by a shark? **Robert Shaw**

16. Is the Kumon Method used in teaching, massage or acupuncture? **Teaching**

17. To what is the ode dedicated that begins: "Thou, who, when fears attack, Bidst them avaunt."? **Tobacco**

18. Which toothpaste was promoted as giving a ring of confidence? **Colgate**

19. What is the subject of the book *Glass's Guide*? **Vehicle prices**

20. True or false: Cleopatra's Needle has nothing to do with Cleopatra? **True**

Quiz 32

1. How many sides has a heptagon? **Seven**

2. What name is given to a pedestrian who crosses roads recklessly? **Jay walker**

3. As a proportional measure, what fraction of a gold object is a carat? **1/24th**

4. What was Telly Savalas' Christian name? Was it Themistocles, Aristotle or Leonidas? **Aristotle**

5. Which six letter word means both to stick to and to part asunder? **Cleave**

6. What kind of flower is a goldilocks? **Buttercup**

7. Wilberforce retired from 10 Downing Street in 1987. Who was he? **A cat**

8. JCB machines are named after Joseph Cyril . . . who? **Bamford**

9. Proverbially, what needs no bush? **Good wine**

10. Who played the title role in the TV serial *Private Schultz*? **Michael Elphick**

11. In which country is Peace River? **Canada**

12. What would you do with a maduro? Would you ride it, smoke it or water it? **Smoke it**

13. Who had Top Ten hits with *Living On the Ceiling*, *Blind Vision* and *Don't Tell Me*? **Blancmange**

14. Who played Hercule Poirot in the 1974 film *Murder on the Orient Express*? **Albert Finney**

15. In which sport, other than skiing, is there a piste? **Fencing**

16. True or false: all thoroughbred racehorses are descended from just three Arab horses? **True**

17. Which kingdom did Alfred the Great rule? **Wessex**

18. What squalid business was called 'Blackbirding'? **Slave Trade**

19. Who was the Roman god of doors and beginnings? **Janus**

20. Whose recent films include *Heartburn*, *The Two Jakes* and *Man Trouble*? **Jack Nicholson's**

Quiz 33

1. What did Colonel Thomas Blood attempt to steal in 1671? **Crown Jewels**

2. Who wrote *Journey to the Centre of the Earth*? **Jules Verne**

3. Which capital city is heated by volcanic springs? Is it Reykjavik, Helsinki or Wellington? **Reykjavik**

4. Whose only No 1 was *I'm Into Something Good*? **Herman's Hermits**

5. Which writer described the 1920s as The Jazz Age? **F Scott Fitzgerald**

6. Who said: "I used to be Snow White but I drifted."? **Mae West**

7. In a classic film, whom did film producer Carl Denham bring to New York and bill as "The Eighth Wonder of the World"? **King Kong**

8. What substance did Lister use to improve the hygiene of surgical operations? **Carbolic Acid**

9. In a poem by Thomas Geat, what was The Pensive Selima? **A cat**

10. Which US playwright wrote *Barefoot in the Park* and *The Odd Couple*? **Neil Simon**

11. In which US state is Little Rock, scene of race riots in 1957? Is it Arkansas, Alabama or South Carolina? **Arkansas**

12. What is America's National Cemetery called? **Arlington**

13. True or false: Arnhem Land is in the Netherlands? **False (It is in Australia.)**

14. Who was Governor of the Bahamas during World War 2? **Duke of Windsor**

15. Whom did New Zealand beat 145-17 in the 1995 Rugby Union World Cup? **Japan**

16. After Windsor, which is the largest castle in Britain? Is it Warwick, Caerphilly or Stirling? **Caerphilly**

17. The pop duo Annie Lennox and Dave Stewart recorded together under what name? **Eurythmics**

18. In which country was Salman Rushdie born? Was it Turkey, India or Malaya? **India**

19. Of which bird did Wordsworth write: "While I am lying on the grass / Thy twofold shout I hear"? **The cuckoo**

20. How did the killer mark his victims in *No Way To Treat a Lady*? **Lipstick kiss on brow**

Quiz 34

1. What was Commonwealth Day called before 1958? **Empire Day**

2. What name is given to expressions like 'catch the town drain' and 'tasted two worms'? **Spoonerism**

3. What are the corns in corned beef? **Salt**

4. Who played the Queen in the 1991 TV play *A Question of Attribution*? **Prunella Scales**

5. Which character from a comic was known as The Pilot of the Future? **Dan Dare**

6. Who was World Darts Champion 5 times between 1980 and 1986? **Eric Bristow**

7. What kind of animal is a Wessex Saddleback? **Pig**

8. Mary O'Brien is the real name of Lulu, Sandie Shaw or Dusty Springfield? **Dusty Springfield**

9. True or false: Dorothea Brooke is the central character of *Middlemarch*? **True**

10. In which country is Encyclopaedia Britannica published? **USA**

11. If you were using English Bond or Flemish Bond what would you be doing? **Bricklaying**

12. In *Gulliver's Travels*, what form did the Yahoos take? **Human form**

13. Which chain of stores was founded by Selim Zilkha in 1961? Was it Mothercare, Next, or Argos? **Mothercare**

14. Whose early days, allegedly, were depicted in the film *Wish You Were Here*? **Cynthia Payne's**

15. Robert Plant was lead singer with which group founded in 1968? **Led Zeppelin**

16. What is the common name for a myocardial infarction? **Heart attack**

17. Is loess a moss, a legal term or a kind of soil? **Soil**

18. 'Run off you girls; boys in view' is a memory aid for what? **The colours of the rainbow**

19. Who directed and starred in the film *Yentl*? **Barbra Streisand**

20. How many cubic centimetres are there in a cubic metre? **One million**

Quiz 35

1. Which locomotive still holds the speed record for steam locomotives? **The *Mallard***

2. Does a pedologist study soils, feet or schoolchildren? **Soils**

3. Which stretch of water separates Denmark from Sweden? **The Kattegat**

4. What is your philtrum? Is it a bone in your ear, a valve in your heart or the groove between nose and top lip? **Groove between nose and lip.**

5. True or false: a gribble is a sea creature? **True (It is a crustacean.)**

6. What is the common name for the garden flower *Dianthus barbatus*? **Sweet William**

7. Complete this Munich quartet: Chamberlain, Hitler, Mussolini and . . .? **Daladier**

8. Upon which town's streets was Monopoly originally based? **Atlantic City's**

9. Which of these did NOT captain England at cricket: Lamb, Boycott or Snow? **Snow**

10. At which battle of 1798 did the boy stand on the burning deck? **Battle of the Nile**

11. For what kind of paintings was Alfred Munnings famous? **Horses**

12. In legend, who was the last King of Troy? **Priam**

13. Which University has a rowing eight called Isis? **Oxford**

14. Mr Tupman, Mr Snodgrass and Mr Winkle were members of which club? **The Pickwick Club**

15. Since 1969 who is the only man, apart from Stephen Hendry, to have won 4 successive World Snooker Championships? **Ray Reardon**

16. Which actor thought he was the man who shot Liberty Valance? **James Stewart**

17. Only two Americans have won the Formula 1 Motor Racing Championship. Name one. **Phil Hill or Mario Andretti**

18. What nationality was the traitor Vidkun Quisling? Was he Norwegian, Danish or Dutch? **Norwegian**

19. What is the collective name for beavers? **Colony**

20. In which town was the Spode pottery works established in the 1760s? Was it Stoke, Derby or Worcester? **Stoke**

Quiz 36

1. True or false: in the radio series the Dales lived in Ambridge? **False (They lived in Kenton and then Exton New Town.)**

2. Which Hindu sect strangled travellers and worshipped Kali? **Thugs**

3. Which country is the major exporter of teak? **Burma (Myanmar)**

4. Which Royal House ruled England from 1461 to 1485? Was it York, Tudor or Stuart? **York**

5. In which TV time travel series does Scott Bakula play the lead? ***Quantum Leap***

6. At which sport was Fred Perry World Champion in 1929? **Table Tennis**

7. Who wrote *The Magus*, *The French Lieutenant's Woman* and *Daniel Martin*? **John Fowles**

8. In Hebrew, does the name Satan mean angel, devil or adversary? **Adversary**

9. Who engaged in the old American custom of bundling? Was it cloth merchants, engaged couples or lawyers? **Engaged couples**

10. Which club won the Scottish FA Cup three times from 1982 to 1984? Was it Celtic, Rangers or Aberdeen? **Aberdeen**

11. Which children's writer, Mrs Heelis, spent 30 years breeding Herdwick sheep? **Beatrix Potter**

12. Of what was the Greek goddess Nyx the personification? **Night**

13. What is smut? Is it a plant disease, a food fish or a duck? **Plant disease**

14. In *Casablanca* who played Sam, the piano player? **Dooley Wilson**

15. Which city, now in West China, is the capital of Tibet? **Lhasa**

16. Which Saint's Feast Day is July 15th? Is it Bartholomew, Martin or Swithin? **Swithin**

17. True or false: the Cat and Mouse Act was used against the suffragettes? **True**

18. In Moscow, what is Tsar Kolokol? **(World's heaviest) Bell**

19. Which club were Division 1 Football League Champions in 1958 and 1959? **Wolverhampton Wanderers**

20. Which Roman palace is one mile west of Chichester? **Fishbourne**

Quiz 37

1. Who wrote the play *Private Lives*? **Noël Coward**

2. From which language does the word Ombudsman come? **Swedish**

3. Who painted the pictures *Irises* and *Sunflowers*? **Van Gogh**

4. Which Chancellor of the Exchequer intoduced the TESSA? **John Major**

5. Whose Top Ten hits included *Rock 'n Roll Winter*, *Are You Ready To Rock?* and *Ball Park Incident*? **Wizzard**

6. Which sportsman would use a fyke? **A fisherman (It is a net.)**

7. Which game featured in the 1980 film *The Baltimore Bullet*? **Pool**

8. Which space telescope was repaired by the shuttle *Endeavour* in 1993? **Hubble**

9. On TV, the Autons, Krotons, Zygons and Voords have all appeared in which series? ***Dr Who***

10. What would you do with kumiss? Would you plaster a wall, drink it or spend it? **Drink it**

11. From 1941, who were forced to wear the Schandband? **Jews (Under Nazi occupation.)**

12. True or false: a locofoco was a self-igniting cigar? **True**

13. What name is given to a petition or protest signed in a circular fashion? **Round Robin**

14. In which building did Prince Charles marry Diana Spencer? **St Paul's Cathedral**

15. The Japanese launched a pre-emptive strike against which country's fleet anchored at Port Arthur in 1904? **Russia's**

16. What destroyed St Pierre on Martinique in 1902? **Volcanic eruption**

17. In the film *The Iron Mistress*, starring Alan Ladd, what was the Iron Mistress? **The bowie knife**

18. Who wrote the 1936 novel *Murder in Mesopotamia*? **Agatha Christie**

19. To which political party did US Presidents W H Harrison, John Tyler and Zachary Taylor belong? **Whig**

20. Who, in the 1970s, was the presenter of *Stars On Sunday* who was nicknamed The Bishop? **Jess Yates**

Quiz 38

1. What did Robert Burns call "great chieftain o' the puddin' race"? **The haggis**

2. How many minutes are there in a degree? **60**

3. From which insect is the antibiotic melitin obtained? Is it a ladybird, a honey-bee or a butterfly? **A honey-bee**

4. What should you find in a camponile? **Bell or bells**

5. Who had Top Ten hits with *Buffalo Stance*, *Manchild* and *7 Seconds*? **Neneh Cherry**

6. What is the other name of the marsh marigold? Is it the kingcup, gillyflower or larkspur? **Kingcup**

7. Who was the first female tennis player to perform the Grand Slam? **Maureen Connolly**

8. Whose last film as director was *Family Plot*? **Alfred Hitchcock**

9. Which Gulf lies between South Yemen and the Horn of Africa? **Gulf of Aden**

10. What did the rat do in the house that Jack built? **Ate the malt**

11. As what was Inigo Jones famous? **Architect**

12. Who played Alf Garnett's daughter? **Una Stubbs**

13. In which Dickens novel do John Jarndyce, Esther Summerson and Lady Dedlock appear? ***Bleak House***

14. Under what name did film star Lee Yuen Kam achieve fame? **Bruce Lee**

15. What does a mendicant do? **Begs**

16. True or false: John Lennon's middle name was Spencer. **False (It was Winston.)**

17. What name is given to the temperature at which heat raises a liquid's temperature no further but converts it to vapour? **Boiling Point**

18. Who collaborated with Karl Marx to produce the Communist Manifesto? **Friedrich Engels**

19. What's the name of the young lion in the film *The Lion King*? **Simba**

20. Which family invented the breech-loading rifle and made typewriters? **Remington**

Quiz 39

1. Who had Top Ten hits with *One Night in Heaven*, *Moving On Up* and *Sight For Sore Eyes*? **M People**

2. What happens at Baikonur, Tyuratam, in Russia? **Space launches**

3. In which Scottish seaside resort did a train go straight through the buffers and out into the street in July 1995? **Largs**

4. In blood, plasma consists of red corpuscles, white corpuscles and what? **Platelets**

5. Whom did Arthur, eldest son of Henry VII, marry in 1501? **Catherine of Aragon**

6. Which Shakespearean character said: "How sharper than a serpent's tooth it is To have a thankless child."? **King Lear**

7. Who wrote *The Edible Woman*, *Life Before Men* and *The Handmaid's Tale*? **Margaret Atwood**

8. Which one word means an abnormal outgrowth on a plant, to chafe or hurt by rubbing, and bitterness of mind? **Gall**

9. Who wrote the *Poldark* stories? **Winston Graham**

10. Whose rules for remembering the directions of magnetic field, current and motion use the fingers? **Fleming's rules**

11. Is Go a type of wrestling, a rank in Bushido or a board game? **Board game**

12. True or false: the name 'bedouin' means 'desert-dweller'? **True**

13. What is an aspen? **A (poplar) tree**

14. Of what are atolls chiefly composed? **Coral**

15. What did Joseph Black discover in 1754 which he called 'fixed air'? **Carbon dioxide**

16. Is a firebrat a metal grate, an insect or a tropical orchid? **Insect**

17. Which TV character worked for the Gateman, Goodbery and Graves Funeral Home? **Herman Munster**

18. Which game was popularised by Ely Culbertson? **Contract Bridge**

19. Which poet said: "I have measured out my life with coffee spoons."? **T S Eliot**

20. Of what is this a definition: 'A style of dance music of black American origin, relying on heavy percussion in polyrhythmic patterns.'? **Funk**

Quiz 40

1. Who was the first signatory of the American Declaration of Independence? **John Hancock**

2. True or false: a 'Cheater' was originally a tax-collector? **True (from Escheator, an officer of the Exchequer)**

3. Who painted the ceiling of the Sistine Chapel? **Michelangelo**

4. Chaka, Dingaan and Cetewayo were leaders of which people? **Zulus**

5. Who wrote *Tropic of Cancer* and *Tropic of Capricorn*? **Henry Miller**

6. In what country is the Algarve? **Portugal**

7. In which film did Bob Hoskins play a black prostitute's minder? ***Mona Lisa***

8. Who, in 1941, designed and made the first viable helicopter? **Sikorsky**

9. Which country's forces were defeated at Poltava by Russia in 1709? **Sweden's**

10. In what country is the port of Archangel? **Russia**

11. What was the setting for the 1984 TV series *Tripper's Day*? **Supermarket**

12. Does 'gravid' mean serious, engraved or pregnant? **Pregnant**

13. To which saint is Westminster Abbey dedicated? **St Peter**

14. In the USA, what does the John Birch Society oppose? **Communism**

15. Would you find an escapement below a rampart, in a castle or in a clock? **In a clock**

16. What is the setting for the opera *Billy Budd*? **A warship**

17. What is the name of the boy in the *Winnie the Pooh* books? **Christopher Robin**

18. In which film does the character Oddjob appear? ***Goldfinger***

19. On which circuit is motor racing's Grand Prix d'Endurance run? **Le Mans**

20. Where in the body would you find a fontanelle? **In the skull**

Quiz 41

1. Which type of camera was invented by Edwin Land in 1947? Was it the Polaroid, the SLR or the Zoom lens? **Polaroid**

2. Which species of tree – mainly – produces cork? **Oak**

3. Which partial peninsula joined with Newfoundland to form Canada's tenth province in 1949? **Labrador**

4. What was Jim Reeves' first Top Ten hit in the UK? Was it *He'll Have To Go, I Love You Because* or *Welcome To My World*? ***Welcome To My World***

5. Which countries formed a military alliance in 1939 called the Pact of Steel? **Italy and Germany**

6. Is a peri an envelope, a covered walk or a fairy? **A fairy**

7. Which Hebridean island was bought by Marlin Eckhard Maruma in 1995? **Eigg**

8. True or false: in the Bible, Potiphar's wife was called Zuleika? **False (She is not named in the Bible.)**

9. In mythology, which giant supported the heavens on his shoulders? **Atlas**

10. What sort of compliment is really a jibe, reproach, insult or criticism? **A back-handed compliment**

11. Which word means a body of hired applauders? **Claque**

12. Which one word means a stick, a unit of measure or a slang word for a gun? **Rod**

13. In which county is Borstal, where the first Youth Custody Centre was set up in 1908? **Kent**

14. Who had Top Ten hits with *Can You Feel the Force* and *Can't Get By Without You*? **The Real Thing**

15. Is a stonecrop a fish, a plant or a bird? **A plant**

16. What is the common name for deuteroscopy? **Second sight**

17. Which woman, famous for her work with wildlife in Africa, was murdered in 1985? **Joy Adamson**

18. In which novel does Quilp, a hunchback moneylender, appear? ***The Old Curiosity Shop***

19. Which seemingly non-existent points were named in 1965 by the Johns Hopkins Applied Physics

Laboratory as being in Ireland, south east of the Cape of Good Hope, west of the Peruvian Coast and between New Guinea and Japan? **The four corners of the Earth**

20. What do succivorous creatures feed on? **Sap**

Quiz 42

1. Where did the Yonghy Bonghy Bo live? **On the Coast of Coromandel (In the middle of the woods)**

2. Which adventure novel featured Gagool, Twala and Umbopa? ***King Solomon's Mines***

3. What was Coco Chanel's Christian name? **Gabrielle**

4. Which American artist is famous for a picture of a can of beans? **Andy Warhol**

5. Which university did the prince attend in *The Student Prince*? **Heidelberg**

6. Does 'Chop Suey' literally mean bits and pieces, fried quickly or vegetable noodles? **Bits and pieces**

7. What is a dirndl? Is it a horse-drawn carriage, a dress, or a form of currency? **Dress**

8. What was the occupation of Jack Ketch? **Hangman**

9. True or false: Sir John Gielgud's first name was George? **False (It was Arthur.)**

10. Who was Russian leader at the time of the Cuban crisis? **Kruschev**

11. What was the first programme shown on Channel 4 on 2nd November 1982? ***Countdown***

12. Which sport featured in the film *The Stratton Story*? Was it ice-hockey, drag-racing or baseball? **Baseball**

13. Who succeeded Albert Reynolds as Prime Minister of Eire? **John Bruton**

14. The Pindus Mountains run north to south through which country? **Greece**

15. For what did the Russian Olga Knipper become famous? **As an actress**

16. Who said: "I've been accused of every death except the casualty list of the World War."? **Al Capone**

17. Which pop group had a hit with *My Generation*? **The Who**

18. From what is the brown pigment bistre prepared? Is it soot, cuttlefish ink or plant roots? **Soot**

19. Who was known as the Iron Chancellor? **Bismarck**

20. Which 16th century astrologer became famous for his obscure prophecies? **Nostradamus**

Quiz 43

1. Are Wu and Min pandas, languages or towns in Malaysia? **Languages**

2. Who played Commissioner Dreyfus in the *Pink Panther* films? **Herbert Lom**

3. Who swam the Hellespont every night to see his lover, Hero? **Leander**

4. Who was the first presenter of *The Golden Shot*? Was it Jackie Rae, Bob Monkhouse or Charlie Williams? **Jackie Rae**

5. In the nursery rhyme "We are all in the dumps, for diamonds are trumps", where have the kittens gone to? **St Paul's**

6. Which one word fits all these definitions: chemise, change of workmen, a trick and a typewriter key for making capitals? **Shift**

7. Which is the largest island just off the west coast of North America? **Vancouver Island**

8. Iodine is necessary for the functioning of which gland? **Thyroid**

9. Which American comedian, known for his meanness, had *Love in Bloom* as his signature tune? **Jack Benny**

10. Who played Toulouse Lautrec in the film *Moulin Rouge*? **José Ferrer**

11. Where do demersal creatures live? Is it in holes, on the seabed or on human skin? **On the seabed**

12. In what year was the Battle of Agincourt? **1415**

13. With what form of transport was Otto Lilienthal associated? Was it gliders, balloons or biplanes? **Gliders**

14. Which Suffolk town, famous for an annual music festival, was the first town in Britain to have a woman mayor? **Aldeburgh**

15. In which country is the source of the Amazon? **Peru**

16. Whom did Anna Anderson claim to be? **Anastasia**

17. What nationality was Anne of Cleves? **German**

18. What is an army worm? Is it a snake, a millipede or a caterpillar? **Caterpillar**

19. Which TV series made Jonathan Routh famous? ***Candid Camera***

20. Who played Dr Phibes in two films? **Vincent Price**

Quiz 44

1. True or false: the alpaca is a hoofed mammal? **True**

2. Alum Bay, Godshill and Carisbrooke Castle are all in which county? **Isle of Wight**

3. Who starred in the Oscar winning films *Quiet Please*, *The Little Orphan* and *The Milky Way*? **Tom and Jerry**

4. Who was the leader of Zanu who became Zimbabwe's first president? **Robert Mugabe**

5. Is varicella the correct name for measles, chickenpox or shingles? **Chickenpox**

6. Where would you wear espadrilles? **On your feet**

7. The Sutherland Falls, among the highest in the world, are in Canada, New Zealand or India? **New Zealand**

8. Who composed *Clair De Lune?* **Debussy**

9. Who starred opposite Fred Astaire in the film *Easter Parade*? **Judy Garland**

10. Which battle of 1645 is said to have cost Charles I his throne? **Naseby**

11. In the Tarzan *stories*, what was the name of Tarzan's monkey friend? **Nkima**

12. Who was the courtier whom Dionysius of Syracuse seated beneath a sword suspended by a human hair? **Damocles**

13. Who was Millard Fillmore? Was he the inventor of Monopoly, the architect of Sydney Opera House or a US President? **US President (1850-52)**

14. What in history was referred to as Black Forty Seven? **Irish Potato Famine (1847)**

15. What was the name of Freddy Laker's cheap transatlantic air service of 1977? **Skytrain**

16. What name is given to the study of language sounds? **Phonetics**

17. True or false: Nancy Reagan was nicknamed The Smiling Mamba? **True**

18. Which town is known as the capital of the Cotswolds? **Cirencester**

19. Which religious movement was founded by John Thomas in 1848? Was it the Seventh Day Adventists, the Plymouth Brethren or the Christadelphians? **The Christadelphians**

20. In which sport are there moves called Triffus, Miller and Rudolf? **Trampolining**

Quiz 45

1. If Monday's child is fair of face, what is Wednesday's child? **Full of woe**

2. Who painted *Snow Storm – Steamboat off a Harbour's Mouth*? **Turner**

3. What was the name of the decorative style of the 1920s and 1930s characterised by geometrical designs and bright metallic surfaces? **Art Deco**

4. In cricket, 111 is believed to be an unlucky score. What is it called? **Nelson**

5. Who was the princess in *Sleeping Beauty*? Was she Aurora, Diana or Flora? **Aurora**

6. Who led the British expedition which conquered Everest in 1953? **John Hunt**

7. Who established the first English printing press in 1476? **William Caxton**

8. By what name is the flower Woodbine better known? **Honeysuckle**

9. Who is the central character in John Braine's book *Room At the Top*? **Joe Lampton**

10. What's the popular name for the constellation Crux? **Southern Cross**

11. Who beat Holland in the 1978 Football World Cup Final? **Argentina**

12. The John Gabel Entertainer appeared in California in 1906. Was it the player piano, the juke box, or the home film projector? **Juke box**

13. True or false: there are 29 books in the New Testament? **False (27)**

14. When Michael Foale became the first Briton to walk in space, what first was achieved by his co-walker, Bernard Harris? **First black man to walk in space**

15. Which sport was founded in Britain on 28th August 1895? Was it Rugby League, Lawn Tennis or Speedway? **Rugby League**

16. In George Orwell's *1984*, what is Britain called? Is it Oceania, Offshore or Airstrip One? **Airstrip One**

17. In which film did Julie Christie win an Oscar playing a model? ***Darling***

18. Which unit amalgamated with the Royal Flying Corps in 1918 to form the RAF? **Royal Naval Air Service**

19. In a famous case, which American spinster was accused of killing her parents in 1892? **Lizzie Borden**

20. In which country was Lady Astor, first woman MP to enter the Commons, born? Was it Canada, America or Australia? **America**

Quiz 46

1. Which insects belong to the order *Diptera*? **(True) Flies**

2. In the Christian Calendar, which immovable feast is celebrated on January 11th? **Baptism of Christ**

3. Which influential comic cartoon series was created by R F Outcault? ***The Yellow Kid***

4. What is Fiordland in New Zealand? **A National Park**

5. Which queen visited Solomon according to I Kings, Chapter 10? **Queen of Sheba**

6. Which British ruler was nicknamed Old Noll? **Oliver Cromwell**

7. Who starred in the films *Blade Runner*, *The Hitcher* and *Flesh and Blood*? **Rutger Hauer**

8. Which country is particularly associated with love-spoons? **Wales**

9. Which sailors were formerly called snotties? **Midshipmen**

10. Which animal is sometimes called the glutton? **Wolverine**

11. In which country did the Stern Gang operate? **Palestine**

12. What was the setting for the TV series *A Very Peculiar Practice*? **(Lowlands) University**

13. Which country were the first European Football Champions (1960)? **USSR**

14. In which city is the University of Surrey? **Guildford**

15. Who said: "I never hated a man enough to give him his diamonds back."? **Zsa Zsa Gabor**

16. Which of the gospels is NOT synoptic? **John's**

17. Who had Top Ten hits with *Is This Love* and *Here I Go Again*? **Whitesnake**

18. Which sport is governed by the WWSU? **Water skiing**

19. In which country was the leader Alexander Dubcek arrested after an invasion by Russia and other Warsaw Pact members? **Czechoslovakia**

20. True or false: there are 12 species of ostrich? **False (1 only)**

Quiz 47

1. What is the correct name for the white of an egg? **Albumen or glair**

2. What adjective means in the manner of, or like, George Bernard Shaw? **Shavian**

3. Which animal has the longest pregnancy? **Elephant**

4. Who had a No 1 hit in 1973 with *Blockbuster*? **Sweet**

5. The watery American and Horseshoe combine to form what? **Niagara Falls**

6. In Shakespeare, who says: "The quality of mercy is not strained."? **Portia**

7. Which TV series, starring Clifford Rose, sprang out of *Secret Army*? ***Kessler***

8. Who was a member of both the winning Men's Doubles and the winning Mixed Doubles at Wimbledon in 1994? **Todd Woodbridge**

9. Which of these was NOT one of the original thirteen American states? Georgia, Maine or Maryland? **Maine**

10. Is tufa a sort of pastry, a kind of rock or an oil extracted from trees? **Rock**

11. In the 16th century, what was the Scavenger's daughter? Was it a torture device, a soup given to paupers or a large bedbug? **Torture device**

12. Who starred in the films *Taps*, *Cocktail* and *Days of Thunder*? **Tom Cruise**

13. Where would you be if you kept referring, in this order, to First, Middle, Morning and Forenoon? **At sea or on a ship**

14. Of which ancient empire was Nineveh the capital? **Assyria**

15. The Houses of York and Lancaster were rival factions of which other Royal House? **Plantaganet**

16. True or false: triquetral and pisiform are bones in the wrist? **True**

17. From which country did Bulgaria gain independence in 1908? Was it Greece, Turkey or Yugoslavia? **Turkey**

18. In the1930s, what name was given to the Central West region of America, mainly Oklahoma and the Dakotas, which suffered drought and high winds? **Dust Bowl**

19. In which European country did Kun's Red Terror exist in 1919? **Hungary**

20. Which famous Jazz Festival, now also known as the JVC Jazz Festival, is held annually in Rhode Island? **Newport Jazz Festival**

Quiz 48

1. Who was the first Roman Emperor? **Augustus**

2. What is TVP usually made from? **Soya**

3. In which novel does Alex undergo psychological experiments known as the Ludovic Technique? ***A Clockwork Orange***

4. Who played the lead in the films *Curly Top*, *Bright Eyes* and *Dimples*? **Shirley Temple**

5. In which county are St Albans, Bishop's Stortford and Hemel Hempstead? **Hertfordshire**

6. On TV, who played Remington Steele? **Pierce Brosnan**

7. Tanjib, Nankeen, Samite, Dornick and Nainsook are all what? **Fabrics**

8. Complete this quotation said by a naval chaplain during the attack on Pearl Harbor: "Praise the Lord and pass the . . . (what)"? **Ammunition**

9. Who was W E Johns' female equivalent of Biggles? **Worrals**

10. Which famous book, first in a series, was subtitled: *The Adventures of a Demobilised Officer Who Found Peace Dull*? ***Bulldog Drummond***

11. What was the nickname of American speculator and philanthropist James Buchanan Brady? **Diamond Jim**

12. Who played Anna in the film *Anna and the King of Siam*? **Irene Dunne**

13. Who had Top Ten hits with *Night Birds* and *Down On the Street*? **Shakatak**

14. Which one word means a sovereign's retinue, to woo and the chamber in which justice is administered? **Court**

15. What does Odeon, from the the Greek oideion, mean? **Theatre**

16. True or false: a fusil was a light musket? **True**

17. Which country surrounds San Marino? **Italy**

18. What name is given to the military tactic of destroying or burning crops and anything that may be of value to an advancing enemy? **Scorched earth policy**

19. Who would use a quern? Would it be a weaver, a miller or a stone-mason? **Miller**

20. What is a davenport? **Sofa or desk**

Quiz 49

1. Which famous greyhound, first to win the Greyhound Derby twice, won 46 of his 61 races? **Mick the Miller**

2. Where was the poet standing when he was inspired to write the poem beginning "Earth has not anything to show more fair"? **Upon Westminster Bridge**

3. What was Barbara Castle's parliamentary constituency? **Blackburn**

4. Who, in the Sermon on the Mount, did Jesus warn would appear as wolves in sheep's clothing? **False prophets**

5. A talbot was often seen in heraldic designs. Was it a griffin, a lion rampant or a dog? **Dog**

6. In which former abbey in Devon can you see Drake's Drum? **Buckland**

7. In mythology, what was odd about Cassandra's prophecies? **Nobody believed them**

8. Who played Gloria in *It Ain't Half Hot, Mum*? **Melvyn Hayes**

9. Which famous book is subtitled *There And Back Again*? ***The Hobbit***

10. What kind of plant is fescue? Is it a grass, a fern or a moss? **Grass**

11. What 'remedy', of no medicinal value, is given to humour a patient? **Placebo**

12. Who became King of England in 1100? **Henry I**

13. What is the capital of the Canadian province of Alberta? **Edmonton**

14. What was the name of the first yacht to win the America's Cup? ***America***

15. What is the common name for the scapula? **Shoulder blade**

16. Is a margay a plant, a tiger-cat or a wave in permed hair? **Tiger-cat**

17. Who was known as The Forces Sweetheart? **Vera Lynn**

18. Which washerwoman did Arthur Lucan play in 14 films and on stage? **Old Mother Riley**

19. Who fronted and devised the TV show *It's A Square World*? **Michael Bentine**

20. What is the relationship between Prince Andrew and Lord Lindley? **They are cousins**

Quiz 50

1. What is Daley Thompson's first name? **Francis**

2. Who had No 1 hits with *Can the Can* and *Devil Gate Drive*? **Suzi Quatro**

3. Which aircraft, piloted by Gary Powers, was shot down by Russia on May 1st 1960? **U-2**

4. Who was Jeanette MacDonald's singing partner in many musical films? **Nelson Eddy**

5. True or false: Operation Overlord was the code-name for Germany's invasion of Russia? **False (Overlord was D-Day.)**

6. Who wrote the biography of Dr Johnson? **James Boswell**

7. Which British city was the first to erect a monument to Lord Nelson? Was it Hereford, Edinburgh or Glasgow? **Glasgow**

8. On which river does Canterbury stand? **Stour**

9. Which monarch wrote the Casket Letters? **Mary, Queen of Scots**

10. Which Christian name is applied to a plane's automatic pilot? **George**

11. Which Oscar winning film of the 1980s was directed by Hugh Hudson? ***Chariots of Fire***

12. Who played the title role in *The Wizard of Oz*? **Frank Morgan**

13. Which chief led the resistance against the Romans in 43 AD? Was it Caractacus, Prasutagus or Madoc? **Caractacus**

14. Which country won the 1992 Olympic Gold medal for baseball? **Cuba**

15. What is the common name for parturition? **Birth or childbirth**

16. In which American state is the Garden of the Gods? **Colorado**

17. Which British football club is known as The Bhoys? **(Glasgow) Celtic**

18. By what name was broadcaster Derek McCulloch better known? **Uncle Mac**

19. Who made her first appearance in *Murder at the Vicarage*? **Miss Marple**

20. Which is the largest theatre in the West End? Is it the Palladium, the Old Vic or the Coliseum? **Coliseum**

Quiz 51

1. Who became MP for Falmouth and Camborne in 1992? **Sebastian Coe**

2. True or false: cockfighting was banned in 1899? **False (1849)**

3. The book subtitled *The Contemplative Man's Recreation* is concerned with what pastime? **Angling**

4. Who devised the package tour? **Thomas Cook**

5. Who played the lead in the TV series *Sorry*? **Ronnie Corbett**

6. Which group had albums called *Fireball* and *Machine Head*? **Deep Purple**

7. To what was Sir Walter Scott referring when he wrote: "Full well I love thy mixed and massy piles."? **Durham Cathedral**

8. Later to be Mrs McAliskey, who became MP for Mid Ulster in 1969? **Bernadette Devlin**

9. Who played the title role in the film *The Prime of Miss Jean Brodie*? **Maggie Smith**

10. What kind of notice puts a block on the publication of information in the interests of security? **D notice**

11. Where can the letters DG REG FD be seen every day? **On coins**

12. Who wrote: "The female of the species is more deadly than the male."? Was it Kipling, Wilde or Pope? **Kipling**

13. What was the nickname of the British 7th Armoured Division in World War 2? **Desert Rats**

14. Which type of bullet was outlawed in 1899? **Dum Dum**

15. With which instrument was Jacqueline Du Pré associated? **Cello**

16. Which programme was presented on radio by Roy Plomley from 1942 to 1985? ***Desert Island Discs***

17. What is the other name of the sword sometimes called Caliburn? **Excalibur**

18. True or false: the Battle of Edgehill was in 1645? **False (1642)**

19. In which story are Ralph, Jack and Peterkin shipwrecked on a desert island? ***The Coral Island***

20. Who is the most famous child of Prince Andrew of Greece and Princess Alice of Battenburg? **Prince Philip**

Quiz 52

1. Spurn Head is at the mouth of which estuary? **Humber**

2. Which member of the cast of *Dad's Army* had a No 1 hit record in November 1970? **Clive Dunn**

3. Which athlete won the 5000m, 10,000m and Marathon at the 1952 Olympics? **Emil Zatopek**

4. What was John Lennon's first solo No 1 in November 1980? ***(Just Like) Starting Over***

5. What name was given to a sickly child left by the fairies in place of a healthy child? **Changeling**

6. Which actor led the sabotage team in *The Guns of Navarone*? **Gregory Peck**

7. In which group of islands is Guadalcanal? **Solomon Islands**

8. In which year was snooker player Steve Davis born? Was it 1957, 1958 or 1959? **1957**

9. Who wrote *I, Claudius* and *Goodbye To All That*? **Robert Graves**

10. On TV, who married Arnold Swain who turned out to be a bigamist? **Emily Bishop**

11. What is indium? Is it a colouring matter, a Greek river or a metallic element? **Element (49)**

12. Which British band had Top Ten hits with *Hot Toddy*, *Skin Deep* and *Swinging Shepherd Blues*? **Ted Heath's Band**

13. Which straits separate the North and South Islands of New Zealand? **Cook Straits**

14. How do you travel if you go by Walker's bus? **You walk**

15. Whom did Paris choose as the most beautiful goddess? **Aphrodite**

16. True or false: St Mark is represented in art by an eagle? **False (Lion)**

17. Whom did Elizabeth I succeed to the throne? **Mary I**

18. Which berries are used to flavour gin? **Juniper**

19. Which US President lived, died and was buried at Mount Vernon, his estate in Virginia? **George Washington**

20. What is the Russian equivalent of John? **Ivan**

Quiz 53

1. What was Limmie's backing group called? **The Family Cookin'**

2. By what name is Frank Pakenham much better known? **Lord Longford**

3. Which is the only species of deer in which both male and female animals have antlers? **Reindeer (or Caribou)**

4. On TV, who played both Robin Hood and the Prince of Moldavia? **Michael Praed**

5. Which animals are attacked by the disease scrapie? **Sheep and goats**

6. Who played the title role in the film *Mrs Miniver*? **Greer Garson**

7. What would you do with soma? Would you eat it, drink it or see a doctor? **Drink it**

8. Who was the mother of Julius Caesar's son, Caesarion? **Cleopatra**

9. Who was the first BBC Sports Personality of the Year in 1954? **Chris Chataway**

10. Which poem begins: "On either side the river lie / Long fields of barley and of rye / That clothe the wold and meet the sky."? ***The Lady of Shallott***

11. With which musical instrument is musician Miles Davis associated? **Trumpet**

12. True or false: Bell Harry is a tower in Canterbury Cathedral? **True**

13. According to legend, what did St Patrick rid Ireland of? **Snakes (Vermin)**

14. Under what name was painter Domenicos Theotokopoulos better known? **El Greco**

15. What were first held at Chamonix in France in 1924? **Winter Olympics**

16. How would you address a cardinal? **Your Eminence**

17. Stephen Crane's novel *The Red Badge of Courage* is set in which war? **US Civil War**

18. Who played the possessed child in the film *The Exorcist*? **Linda Blair**

19. Who was the first English Monarch to be called Defender of the Faith? **Henry VIII**

20. Who composed the film scores for *Henry V*, *Hamlet* and *Richard III*? **William Walton**

Quiz 54

1. Who had Top Ten hits with *Sugar Candy Kisses* and *Don't Do It, Baby*? **Mac and Katie Kissoon**

2. In Norfolk, is a dodman a donkey, a mole or a snail? **A snail**

3. In which country are Theron Airways based? Is it South Africa, Bulgaria or Greece? **South Africa**

4. Who designed The Monument? **Christopher Wren**

5. In 1983, who played the title role on TV in *Reilly, Ace of Spies*? **Sam Neill**

6. Which creatures warned the Capitol in Rome of a night attack by the Gauls in 390 BC? **Geese**

7. Which great pop star of the 1950s had the first names Charles Hardin? **Buddy Holly**

8. True or false: Misr is what Egyptians call Egypt? **True**

9. Proverbially, what should you not put in one basket? ***All* your eggs**

10. What would you find in Sankey and Moody's famous book first published in 1873? **Hymns**

11. Of which country was Wilfried Martens Prime Minister several times from 1979? **Belgium**

12. Which country resigned from the Commonwealth in 1961? **South Africa**

13. Which actress, born Billie Cassin, was also known as Lucille Le Sueur? **Joan Crawford**

14. Whose law states that the potential difference in an electric current is equal to the product of the current flowing and the resistance? **Ohm's Law**

15. In the 1956 Olympics, held in Australia, which events were held in Sweden? **Equestrian**

16. On TV, who played the fat detective, Cannon? **William Conrad**

17. Which common substance was once called Eisel? Was it diesel fuel, vinegar or bleach? **Vinegar**

18. Which British actor said: "When I played drunks, I had to remain sober because I didn't know how to play them when I was drunk."? **Richard Burton**

19. Who had Top Ten hits with *Long Tall Glasses*, *Moonlighting* and *More Than I Can Say*? **Leo Sayer**

20. Sluys was the first and Castillon was the last battle in which war? **100 Years War**

Quiz 55

1. Who played the Jackal in *The Day of the Jackal*? **Edward Fox**

2. With what is the society called EXIT concerned? Is it Euthanasia, Emigration or Divorce? **Euthanasia**

3. Which pop singer and actor was born Terry Nelhams? **Adam Faith**

4. When Argentinians landed on South Georgia in 1982 what had they supposedly come to collect? **Scrap metal**

5. What was the name of the dog in Enid Blyton's *Famous Five* books? Was it George, Timmy or Monty? **Timmy**

6. Which Hampshire air show is held biennially in September? **Farnborough**

7. Which British boxer lost to Joe Louis on points in 1937 when fighting for the World Heavyweight Title? **Tommy Farr**

8. Who conducted the famous TV interview series *Face To Face*? **John Freeman**

9. Who coined the phrase "a land fit for heroes to live in"? Was it Asquith, Bonar Law or Lloyd George? **Lloyd George**

10. Whose collected plays were published in the *First Folio*? **Shakespeare's**

11. Which pop group was formed by Roy Wood in 1971 and had No 1 albums with *Time* and *Discovery*? **ELO**

12. Who was the bully in the book *Tom Brown's Schooldays*? **Flashman**

13. What was the name of Harry Llewellyn's gold-medal-winning horse in the 1952 Olympics? **Foxhunter**

14. True or false: a crucian is a type of cross? **False (It is a fish.)**

15. Which poet is buried in Grasmere churchyard? **Wordsworth**

16. Which city did the Romans call Glevum? Was it Gloucester, Glasgow or Liverpool? **Gloucester**

17. Which Treasury Minister was murdered by an IRA bomb outside his home in 1990? **Ian Gow**

18. In which comedy TV series did Ballard Berkeley play Major Gowen? ***Fawlty Towers***

19. For what was Beryl Grey famous? Was it Opera, Ballet or Sculpture? **Ballet**

20. In ballet what is a 'sauté'? **A plain jump in the air**

Quiz 56

1. Who played the title role in *Gandhi* in 1982? **Ben Kingsley**

2. The current Duke of St Albans is a direct descendant of Charles II's mistress. Who was she? **Nell Gwynn**

3. Which sea lies between the Bosporus and the Dardanelles? **Sea of Marmara**

4. Who became Nelson's mistress and bore him a child in 1801? **Lady Hamilton**

5. Who wrote *The Good Companions*? Was it G B Shaw, J B Priestley or Oscar Wilde? **J B Priestley**

6. Which handicapped physicist wrote *A Brief History of Time*? **Stephen Hawking**

7. With what does *Grove's Dictionary* deal? Is it the clergy, music or word derivations? **Music**

8. Which literary family lived at Haworth in Yorkshire? **The Brontës**

9. Tartan Khan, I'm Slippy and Tico have all won what famous race? **Greyhound Derby**

10. What were once kept in a patch box? Was it odd pieces of material, fancy eye-patches or beauty spots and patches? **Beauty spots and patches**

11. Which famous dancing troupe was formed by Margaret Kelly? **Bluebell Girls**

12. Who hosted the radio quiz show *Have a Go*? **Wilfrid Pickles**

13. Which Public School's school song begins: "Forty years on, when far and asunder"? **Harrow**

14. In which famous adventure story is Harry Faversham the central character? ***The Four Feathers***

15. What is a gibus? Is it a collapsible top hat, a type of monkey or an ancient sailing ship? **Collapsible top hat**

16. In which part of the British Isles would you find bailiwicks? **Channel Isles**

17. How long is a dog watch at sea? **Two hours**

18. What legal-sounding name is given to a temporary mast rigged at sea? **Jury mast**

19. Which murderer lived at 10 Rillington Place? **John Christie**

20. What product did Mary Holland spend 18 years advertising on TV? **Oxo**

Quiz 57

1. Who made the first cross-Channel flight in 1909? **Louis Blériot**

2. In which film did Tom Cruise take Dustin Hoffman to Las Vegas? ***Rain Man***

3. Where was the German fleet scuttled in 1919? **Scapa Flow**

4. Who had a mountain retreat at Berchtesgaden? **Hitler**

5. Whose only No 1 hit was *Barbados* in 1975? **Typically Tropical**

6. How many named people went to Widdicombe Fair with Uncle Tom Cobbleigh and the singer? **Six**

7. In *Brookside*, who was buried under the patio? **Trevor Jordache**

8. Who wrote *The Count of Monte Cristo*? **Alexandre Dumas**

9. True or false: Hughie Greene presented the TV series *Take Your Pick*? **False (It was Michael Miles.)**

10. Which people worshipped the rain god Apu Ilapu? Was it the Cherokee, the Incas or the Mongols? **Incas**

11. What sort of creature was Chewbacca in *Star Wars*? **A Wookey**

12. What was the name of Emile Ford's backing group? **The Checkmates**

13. How often does the phoenix rise from the ashes? **Every 500 years**

14. Which capital city's name means 'meeting of the muddy waters'? Is it Kuala Lumpur, Rangoon or Bangkok? **Kuala Lumpur**

15. What is your columella? Is it the tip of your ear, your eyelid or the skin that separates your nostrils? **Skin separating nostrils**

16. What makes stainless steel stainless? **Chromium**

17. In which city is the Fitzwilliam Museum? **Cambridge**

18. Whose address was No1, London? Was it Gladstone's, the Duke of Wellington's or George I's? **Duke of Wellington's**

19. What was the main wood used by Thomas Chippendale in the 18th century? Was it rosewood, boxwood or mahogany? **Mahogany**

20. In what year was poison gas used in war for the first time? Was it 1915, 1916 or 1917? **1915**

Quiz 58

1. What did the B stand for in Cecil B De Mille? **Blount**

2. For what was the Dutch town of Delft particularly famous? **Pottery**

3. In English Literature, why is Sergeant Cuff famous? **First fictional detective**

4. The canine disease 'hard pad' is a form of which disease? **Distemper**

5. Who wrote the novels *Vivian Grey*, *Sybil* and *Endymion*? **Benjamin Disraeli**

6. Is a culverin a bird, a gun or a plant? **Gun**

7. Which is the lowest rank in the ministry of the Christian Church? **Deacon**

8. Which former English head of state lived in Paris as John Clarke from 1660 to 1680? **Richard Cromwell**

9. What did a crossbow fire? **Bolt or quarrel**

10. Which was the last land battle fought in Britain? **Culloden**

11. In sport, what was said to have died on 29th August 1882? **English cricket**

12. What name was given to the operation to lay oil pipelines under the English Channel in World War 2? **Pluto**

13. Which black actor starred in *The Defiant Ones, Lilies of the Field* and *Edge of the City*? **Sidney Poitier**

14. In poker, what name is given to a hand containing a pair and three of a kind? **Full House**

15. What is the next prime number after 73? **79**

16. The Cherry Hill System was adopted in Britain in the 1840s in what area? **Prisons**

17. If something is piliferous what does it have? **Hairs**

18. In what year was prohibition repealed in the USA? **1933**

19. How many eyes does a senocular spider have? **Six**

20. To what purpose is a Very pistol put? **To fire flares or rockets**

Quiz 59

1. Which British Prime Minister was known as The Great Commoner? **William Pitt (Elder)**

2. In fiction, who created the detective Auguste Dupin? **Edgar Allan Poe**

3. For what did Ponce De Leon search in 1513? **Fountain of Youth**

4. On which TV magazine did Ian Harmon replace Joanne Minster as editor? ***Compact***

5. Which TV series had the character Yosser Hughes? ***Boys From the Blackstuff***

6. Alexander Selkirk's experiences formed the basis of which famous book? ***Robinson Crusoe***

7. Alexander the Great said: "If I were not Alexander, I should wish to be . . . (who)"? **Diogenes**

8. Which famous survey was begun in 1086? ***Domesday Book***

9. What sort of entertainer is a siffleur? **Whistler**

10. Who had a No 1 with *Cars* in 1979? **Gary Numan**

11. If you were travelling from London to Cardiff, from which mainline station would you catch a train? **Paddington**

12. Which US state is named after the wife of Charles I? **Maryland**

13. Who completed the men's sprint double at the 1972 Olympics? **Valeri Borzov**

14. By what name is the Deutsche Dogge known outside Germany? **Great Dane**

15. What part of the body consumes 40% of the blood's oxygen? **Brain**

16. Which British poet has his own National Day? **Robert Burns**

17. Who started the *Today* newspaper? **Eddie Shah**

18. On TV, what was Margaret Houlihan's nickname? **Hot Lips**

19. Which Marx Brothers film featured the famous cabin scene? ***A Night at the Opera***

20. In which Commonwealth country did the Mau Mau operate? **Kenya**

Quiz 60

1. Freddy Mercury took *The Great Pretender* into the charts in 1987, but which group had a hit with it in 1956? **The Platters**

2. Which character did Richard Burton play in the film *Cleopatra*? **Mark Antony**

3. In which city was the TV series *Shoestring* set? **Bristol**

4. Which Scottish king died of leprosy? **Robert the Bruce**

5. Which country did Russia invade in 1956? **Hungary**

6. Who won the 1942 Nobel Peace Prize? **No one**

7. Which is the only country crossed by both the Tropic of Capricorn and the Equator? **Brazil**

8. On which course did Tony Jacklin win the British Open Golf championship in 1969? **Royal Lytham St Anne's**

9. In the binary system, what would 100 represent? **4**

10. In which castle is *Hamlet* set? **Elsinore**

11. In *Gulliver's Travels*, from what did silly scientists seek to extract sunshine? **Cucumbers**

12. Who said in Paris in 1900: "I am dying beyond my means."? **Oscar Wilde**

13. Which TV soap opera was set in the village of King's Oak? ***Crossroads***

14. Of which colleague did Harold Wilson say: "He immatures with age."? **Tony Benn**

15. Which robber did Pontius Pilate release instead of Jesus? **Barabbas**

16. On what is the Mona Lisa's right hand resting? **Her left hand**

17. In what game might you use the Sicilian Defence? **Chess**

18. Which element is present in all organic compounds? **Carbon**

19. Who, in a poem by Keats, "stood in tears amid the alien corn"? **Ruth**

20. What did Britain abolish on 18th December 1969? **Death penalty**

Quiz 61

1. In which US state is the Painted Desert? **Arizona**

2. Which Indian city is served by Dum Dum airport? **Calcutta**

3. Which TV series featured British women in a Japanese prison camp? ***Tenko***

4. On which British golf course is the Postage Stamp hole? **Troon**

5. What element is brimstone the old name for? **Sulphur**

6. Who played the captain of the starship USS *Enterprise* in the first episode of *Star Trek*? **Jeffrey Hunter**

7. Which disease affects the parotid salivary gland? **Mumps**

8. In one story, what did Apollo give to King Midas? **Ass's ears**

9. At which famous battle did Miltiades command the winning side? **Marathon**

10. In which European country is the region of Campania? **Italy**

11. In which city are the cricket and rugby grounds known as Newlands? **Cape Town**

12. In what game could a player roll his bonce at an alley? **Marbles**

13. What sort of a creature is a Sooty Mangabey? **A monkey**

14. To which political party did Robert Walpole belong? **Whig**

15. Which fruit is a cross of a peach and a plum? **Nectarine**

16. What sporting target is 28 inches high and 9 inches wide? **Cricket wicket**

17. Lake Bala is the largest natural lake in which country? **Wales**

18. Who is buried at the Arc de Triomphe? **Unknown Soldier**

19. Which film cowboy rode a horse called Tony? **Tom Mix**

20. Which political group used to drink a toast to The Little Gentleman in Velvet? **Jacobites**

Quiz 62

1. In fiction, which eponymous hero died at Fort Zinderneuf? **Beau Geste**

2. Who was the last Emperor of India? **George VI**

3. Which planet is sometimes called the evening star? **Venus**

4. In which city is Scottish football team St Johnstone based? **Perth**

5. In which country was bingo first played? **Italy**

6. Who had Top Ten hits in the1960s with *Nine Times Out of Ten*, *Gee Whiz, It's You* and *A Girl Like You*? **Cliff Richard**

7. Which famous author was tricked in 1922 by two girls' fakc photographs of fairies? **Sir Arthur Conan Doyle**

8. Which horror story and film is set in the isolated Overlook Hotel where a caretaker gradually goes mad? ***The Shining***

9. In mythology, on which island did the Minotaur live? **Crete**

10. In pounds, shillings and pence, why did D represent pennies or pence? **From denarius**

11. In *Coronation Street*, who was Bet's deadly rival, the landlady of The White Swan? **Stella Rigby**

12. Off which UK island are The Needles? **Isle of Wight**

13. Which two countries are separated by the Torres Strait? **Australia and Papua New Guinea**

14. What was the name of the Cisco Kid's horse? **Diablo**

15. What sort of entertainer is a diseur or diseuse? **Reciter of monologues**

16. Who would use the terms pavilion, culasse, culet and table? **Diamond (gem) cutter**

17. Who composed the opera *Pelleas et Melisande*? **Debussy**

18. In *Wuthering Heights*, whom did Catherine Earnshaw marry? **Edgar Linton**

19. What is hippocras? **Spicy wine**

20. Of which US state is Olympia the state capital? **Washington**

Quiz 63

1. In 1926 Gertrude Ederle was the first woman to do what? **Swim the English Channel**

2. From which animal does cashmere come? **A goat**

3. In the Sci Fi novel *Fahrenheit 451*, what did firemen do? **Burn books**

4. Which film star's biography was called *Neither Shaken Nor Stirred*? **Sean Connery's**

5. True or false: Casanova was Italian? **True**

6. In which country would you be if you landed at Dalaman airport? **Turkey**

7. The mythical creature a silkie is half man half . . . (what)? **Seal**

8. What was the official residence of British sovereigns from 1698 until 1837? **St James's Palace**

9. Off which South American port was the Graf Spee scuttled in 1939? **Montevideo**

10. What is the name of the big cannon in Edinburgh Castle? **Mons Meg**

11. Which word means one tenth of a nautical mile? **Cable**

12. What is the minimum age a US President has to be? **35**

13. If you were lapidated, what would happen to you? **You would be stoned to death**

14. Which was the first British National Park? **Peak District**

15. Apart from Galahad, two other knights achieved the Holy Grail. Name one. **Bors or Percival**

16. Which chemical element is found in all proteins? Is it carbon, oxygen or nitrogen? **Nitrogen**

17. Which fruit has the Latin name prunus persica? Is it the peach, the plum or the damson? **Peach**

18. What nationality was the composer Rachmaninov? **Russian**

19. A musket ball fired from the French ship *Redoubtable* killed which famous Englishman? **Lord Nelson**

20. What would you expect in a pluvial region? **Rain**

Quiz 64

1. True or false: St Austell is in Cornwall? **True**
2. Who was the first negro boxer to be World Heavyweight Champion? **Jack Johnson**
3. What attracted many Americans to the Sioux's sacred Black Hills in the 1860s? **Gold**
4. After sheltering from a storm near Cheddar Gorge, Augustus Toplady wrote which hymn? ***Rock of Ages***
5. What was the title of the book about the Watergate scandal written by Washington Post reporters Bernstein and Woodward? ***All the President's Men***
6. In the film *Who Framed Roger Rabbit?*, what was Roger's wife called? **Jessica**
7. You would use dannocks if you were hedging. What are they? **Thick gloves**
8. Where is the Chester Beatty Library? Is it in Perth, Dublin or Cardiff? **Dublin**
9. In what capacity did the writer Ernest Hemingway serve in World War 1? **Ambulance driver**
10. Who broke Roger Bannister's mile record? **John Landy**
11. Schnauzer is a breed of which animal? **Dog**
12. Who wrote the music for the ballet *Les Sylphides*? Was it Chopin, Tchaikovsky or Mozart? **Chopin**
13. In which city are the Spanish Steps? **Rome**

14. Who was the oldest woman to sit in the House of Commons? Was it Bessie Braddock, Irene Ward or Barbara Castle? **Irene Ward**

15. What is kelp? **Seaweed**

16. How long did Mary Poppins say she would stay with the children? **Until the wind changed**

17. True or false: Andrew was the brother of Simon, called Peter? **True**

18. Metric crown, metric demy and metric royal are different sizes of what? **Paper**

19. What name is sometimes given to the legislative assembly of a country that is derived from the Latin for old man? **Senate**

20. Who dined on mince and slices of quince? **The Owl and the Pussycat**

Quiz 65

1. If you ordered pamplemousse in a French restaurant, what would you get? **Grapefruit**

2. From the 14th century to 1830 the eldest sons of French kings were known by what title? **Dauphin**

3. After Pacific, Atlantic and Indian, which is the next largest ocean? **Arctic**

4. Why was General Claus von Stauffenberg executed in 1944? **He tried to assassinate Hitler**

5. What is the name for food permissible under Moslem dietary laws? **Halal**

6. Which saint's cathedral is in Moscow's Red Square? **St Basil's**

7. With which sport is Wayne Gretzky associated? **Ice Hockey**

8. Marble is formed by the metamorphosis of which rock? Is it limestone, sandstone or granite? **Limestone**

9. Which English composer wrote a *Sea Symphony* and a *London Symphony*? **Ralph Vaughan Williams**

10. Where did methyl isocyanate cause 2,600 deaths in 1984? **Bhopal in India**

11. How many cards are there in a tarot pack? Is it 64, 72 or 78? **78**

12. What character was played by Peter Sellers in the film *I'm Alright, Jack*? **Fred Kite**

13. In which city was Europe's first hard paste porcelain made? Was it Dresden, Worcester or Meissen? **Dresden**

14. Who had No 1 hits with *Tired of Waiting For You* and *Sunny Afternoon*? **Kinks**

15. Who wrote the book *Schindler's Ark*? **Thomas Kenneally**

16. What is the name of the bass tuba that wraps around the player's body? **Sousaphone**

17. Which is the largest English national park? Is it Dartmoor, Exmoor or the Lake District? **Lake District**

18. Who said: "There are only two kinds of music; good and bad."? **Duke Ellington**

19. Which acid builds up in the muscles during strenuous exercise? **Lactic Acid**

20. True or false: Utah is nicknamed The Waterfall State? **False (Beehive State)**

Quiz 66

1. Who was the little boy brought up by wolves in *The Jungle Book*? **Mowgli**

2. Who was King of France at the time of the French Revolution? **Louis XVI**

3. What makes green pasta green? Is it broccoli, cabbage or spinach? **Spinach**

4. What is the name for a person who will eat no food of animal origin? **Vegan**

5. Which element is found in bones, teeth and shells? **Calcium**

6. Which pop singer played the title role in the film *Tommy*? **Roger Daltrey**

7. What is a booby? Is it a tropical fish, a tropical bird or a tropical lizard? **Tropical bird**

8. The playwright Pirandello wrote a play called *Six Characters in Search of an* . . . (what)? ***Author***

9. Is the Great Wall of China 1250, 1450 or 1650 miles long? **1450 miles**

10. Who first said: "A week is a long time in politics."? **Harold Wilson**

11. Who has produced CDs called *Tell Mama*, *Seven Year Itch* and *Stickin' To My Guns*? **Etta James**

12. Is an apse a poisonous snake, part of a church or an acidic fruit? **Part of a church**

13. What kind of wild cattle with shaggy coats and upturned horns live in the mountains of Tibet? **Yaks**

14. Which carbohydrate makes jam gel? **Pectin**

15. Who had Top Ten hits in the 1960s with *Calendar Girl*, *I Go Ape* and *Little Devil*? **Neil Sedaka**

16. True or false: a manometer measures the pressure of liquids? **True**

17. Which record producer created the Wall of Sound for the Crystals and Ronettes? **Phil Spector**

18. After which frontier scout was the capital of Nevada named? **Kit Carson**

19. Which river flows for 1500 miles through Venezuela, forming part of the border with Colombia? Is it the Amazon, the Orinoco or the Rio de la Plata? **Orinoco**

20. What would you use if you practised ikebana? **Flowers**

Quiz 67

1. What type of novels were written by Zane Grey? **Westerns**

2. Which animals were dachshunds originally bred to hunt? **Badgers**

3. Who played the witch-wife in the TV series *Bewitched*? **Elizabeth Montgomery**

4. Which many-headed monster's blood killed Hercules? **Hydra**

5. What is the collective name for rain, snow, hail and sleet? **Precipitation**

6. In which Italian city is Michelangelo's statue of David? Is it Florence, Venice or Rome? **Florence**

7. Which famous American's two year old son was kidnapped and murdered in 1932? **Charles Lindbergh's**

8. Who had a 1966 hit with *Good Vibrations*? **Beach Boys**

9. With what is the Birkenhead Drill concerned? **Women and children first in lifeboats**

10. Which medical device was invented by Dr Rene Laennec to preserve his female patients' modesty? **Stethoscope**

11. Which part of the body contains the choroid, sclera and fovea? **Eye**

12. True or false: Sir Robert Helpmann was Australian? **True**

13. Which Italian expression meaning 'in the church style' denotes unaccompanied singing? **A cappella**

14. Whom did Achilles kill and drag round Troy behind his chariot? **Hector**

15. Which is the fifth book of the New Testament? **Acts of the Apostles**

16. Which flavouring is added to brandy and egg yolks to make advocaat? Is it aniseed, zest of oranges or vanilla? **Vanilla**

17. What colour is a kingfisher's egg? **White**

18. Which part of the body is affected by osteomyelitis? **Bones**

19. What nationality was Alan Paton, author of *Cry, the Beloved Country*? **South African**

20. What is a durmast? Is it a fruit, a tree or a songbird? **Tree (oak)**

Quiz 68

1. In which art form did German-born Ernst Lubitsch gain fame? **Cinema**

2. Which is Poland's largest river? Is it the Oder, the Dvina or the Vistula? **Vistula**

3. Which boxer's real name was Walker Smith? **Sugar Ray Robinson's**

4. Which was the first Harry Palmer film? ***The Ipcress File***

5. In which city did Anne Frank write her diary? **Amsterdam**

6. Edward de Vere, 17th Earl of Oxford, has sometimes been suggested as the real author of what? **Shakespeare's works**

7. Who set stories in the imaginary county of Barsetshire? **Anthony Trollope**

8. True or false: Catherine Parr never re-married after Henry VIII's death? **False (She married Thomas Seymour.)**

9. Which Top Ten hit of 1962 contained these lines: "There's more than 7 wonders in this world: I've just met No 8."? ***Venus in Blue Jeans***

10. Who wrote the TV series *Curry and Chips*? **Johnny Speight**

11. What is the family name of the Dukes of Northumberland? **Percy**

12. With which country do you associate Test Cricketer Heath Streak? **Zimbabwe**

13. Which artist painted 62 self portraits? Was it Van Gogh, Rembrandt or Picasso? **Rembrandt**

14. Which writer created The Saint? **Leslie Charteris**

15. What is xerography? Is it writing about foreigners, the x-ray process or photocopying? **Photcopying**

16. John Bellingham shot and killed whom in the House of Commons in 1812? **Spencer Perceval**

17. Who was King Solomon's mother? **Bathsheba**

18. Which war began on June 25th, 1950? **Korean**

19. Who played the police chief in the film *Jaws*? **Roy Scheider**

20. *The Outlaw*, *The Conqueror*, *The Good* and *The Fourth* were all descriptions in the titles of books about which rascal? **William Brown**

Quiz 69

1. On which river is Balmoral Castle? **Dee**

2. When was the wearing of front seat belts made compulsory? 1982, 1983 or 1984? **1983**

3. Which is the lightest known substance? **Hydrogen**

4. True or false: XCI are the Roman numerals for 111? **False (91)**

5. Whom did Sherlock Holmes refer to as THE Woman? **Irene Adler**

6. What was the major event that took place at Golgotha? **Christ's crucifixion**

7. What would you do with a futon: eat it, wear it or sleep on it? **Sleep on it**

8. Which English playwright was murdered by his lover, Kenneth Halliwell, in 1967? **Joe Orton**

9. Whose *Born In the USA* album was a massive bestseller in 1985? **Bruce Springsteen's**

10. Which animal was traditionally called 'Russell'? **Fox**

11. Which English queen died of smallpox at the age of 32? **Mary II**

12. Which German city was the target of the first 1000-bomber raid? Was it Dresden, Hamburg or Cologne? **Cologne**

13. Which creatures collect in a clowder? **Cats**

14. How long does it take the Earth to travel one and a half million miles? Is it a day, a week or a month? **A day**

15. In which country is Transylvania? **Romania**

16. Which character did David Jason play in *Porridge*? **Blanco**

17. Who won the Women's London Marathon in 1984 and 1985? **Ingrid Christianson**

18. In which English city was the first Salvation Army brass band formed? Was it Derby, Oxford or Salisbury? **Salisbury**

19. Which international footballer is commemorated in two stained-glass windows at St Francis's Church in Dudley, near his home? **Duncan Edwards**

20. Which American star played a teacher in *Ryan's Daughter*? **Robert Mitchum**

Quiz 70

1. Who had a No 1 hit in 1977 with *So You Win Again*? **Hot Chocolate**

2. In which film did Bruce Willis destroy an airliner with his cigarette lighter? ***Die Hard* 2**

3. Which playwright wrote *Roots*, *Chicken Soup With Barley* and *Chips With Everything*? **Arnold Wesker**

4. St Austell in Cornwall is a centre for the production of which raw material? **China Clay**

5. Which is the smallest species of the partridge family? **Quail**

6. Who commanded the forgotten 14th army in Burma in World War 2? **William Slim**

7. What did Felix Wankel develop in the 1950s? **(Rotary) Petrol engine**

8. The North American mountain lion is known by three other names. Give one. **Puma or cougar or catamount**

9. What transports moraine? **A glacier**

10. Who was the last Aztec Emperor? **Montezuma II**

11. Which form of sugar is found in solution in milk? **Lactose**

12. For what was the priest Gerard Manley Hopkins famous? **Poetry**

13. Which film star was nicknamed The King of Hollywood? **Clark Gable**

14. In which 1986 TV series did Paul McGann play Percy Topliss, a crook and impersonator? ***The Monocled Mutineer***

15. What is bohea? **(Inferior) Tea**

16. What is a corn-cockle? **A flower**

17. Which capital city in Europe stands on the islands of Zealand and Armager? **Copenhagen**

18. To which family of birds does the condor belong? **Vulture**

19. Which US pop group, formed in 1964, included Roger McGuinn, David Crosby, Gene Clark, Chris Hillman and Michael Clarke? **The Byrds**

20. Who is the hereditary spiritual leader of the Ismaili sect of Muslims? **The Aga Khan**

Quiz 71

1. Who won Best Director Oscar for the film *Reds* in 1981? **Warren Beatty**

2. By what name is acetylsalicylic acid better known? **Aspirin**

3. In the bible, what does the word 'Adam' mean? **Man**

4. Which licences were introduced in 1796 and abolished in 1988? **Dog licences**

5. In politics, what word is used for rearranging constituency boundaries for unfair advantage? **Gerrymandering**

6. The Jacuzzi was originally developed for the treatment of which complaint? **Arthritis**

7. From which animal is lard mainly produced? **Pig**

8. In what year was the Magna Carta granted by King John? **1215**

9. To an American it's Plexiglass. What do we call it? **Perspex**

10. What is the popular name for the Strategic Defence Initiative? **Star Wars**

11. Who partnered Peter Sellers on the Top Ten hit *Goodness Gracious Me*? **Sophia Loren**

12. Where would you find the Quirinal, Viminal and Aventine Hills? **Rome**

13. What is yaws? **A tropical disease**

14. What was the world's first viewdata system called? **Prestel**

15. Which musical term means 'played so that the bow rebounds lightly from the strings'? **Spiccato**

16. Which female MP was a founder member of the SDP? **Shirley Williams**

17. US Admiral Kummel and Lieutenant General Short were relieved of their posts as a result of which infamous attack? **Pearl Harbor**

18. Who created the literary character Allan Quatermain? **H Rider Haggard**

19. Which area of London contains The Royal Hospital, The National Army Museum and the Physic Garden? **Chelsea**

20. Who was USSR President from 1983 to 1984? **Yuri Andropov**

Quiz 72

1. What is the opposite of aestivation? **Hibernation**

2. Which country's troops occupied Lima in 1881? **Chile's**

3. In *Coronation Street*, who is Vicky MacDonald's grandfather? **Alec Gilroy**

4. John Flamsteed was the first man to hold which starry post? **Astronomer Royal**

5. Which Hebrew prophet was carried up to heaven in a fiery chariot? **Elijah**

6. What is a brittle star? **Starfish**

7. At which battle in 1690 did William III defeat James II? **Battle of the Boyne**

8. Which is the most easterly port in Britain? **Lowestoft**

9. Who abdicated the Dutch throne in 1980? **Queen Juliana**

10. From what did the ancient soothsayer, the haruspex, foretell the future? **Entrails**

11. Which Dickens novel features the characters Mr Dick, Little Em'ly and Uriah Heep? ***David Copperfield***

12. Who played the title role in the 1953 film *Houdini*? **Tony Curtis**

13. Which town is regarded as Edinburgh's port? **Leith**

14. Which speaker of the House of Commons became Viscount Tonypandy? **George Thomas**

15. Which Government Department has its HQ at 50 Queen Anne's Gate? **Home Office**

16. After whom was pop star Chubby Checker named? **Fats Domino**

17. Which of these films did NOT win Best Picture Oscar: *Gandhi*, *Amadeus*, *Klute* and *Platoon*? ***Klute***

18. Which Sci Fi writer produced the *Dune* saga? **Frank Herbert**

19. Who played Suzi Kettles in the TV series *Tutti Frutti*? **Emma Thompson**

20. What is made from the paste, strass? **Imitation jewels**

Quiz 73

1. True or false: the Stretford End is at Edgbaston? **False (It is at Old Trafford.)**

2. Who was the last prisoner to be held in the Tower of London? **Rudolf Hess**

3. In which book did people find Shangri-La? ***Lost Horizon***

4. Which amber globe was named after a 1930s' Minister of Transport? **Belisha Beacon**

5. What did baker John Faynor's carelessness cause? **The Fire of London**

6. Who played M in the Bond film *Goldeneye*? **Judi Dench**

7. Where is the most famous colony of Macaque Monkeys? **Gibraltar**

8. Captain Bligh was elected a fellow of the Royal Society for services to what? **Navigation and botany**

9. Which punk musician's real name was Simon Ritchie? **Sid Vicious**

10. Who drew the Mister Men? **Roger Hargreaves**

11. From whom did the animals seize the farm in *Animal Farm*? **Mr Jones**

12. Which creature's Latin name is *bufo bufo*? **Toad**

13. What is the correct name for the high jump event in showjumping? **Puissance**

14. Which ship sent the first SOS? ***Titanic***

15. When was decimal currency introduced in Britain? **1971**

16. What was the name of Guy Gibson's dog? **Nigger**

17. True or false: a VLCC is an oil tanker? **True**

18. Is a belvedere a bluebell, a viewing turret or an old name for a badger? **Viewing turret**

19. Into which river did the Pied Piper lead the rats? Was it the Elbe, Rhine or Weser? **Weser**

20. What is the common name for the psychological Rorschasch Test? **Ink blot test**

Quiz 74

1. What is the capital of Australia? **Canberra**

2. In *Dad's Army*, what was Private Fraser's daytime job? **Undertaker**

3. Which wine is flavoured with pine resin? **Retsina**

4. Which of these plants produces most food per acre? Is it pineapple, banana or melon? **Banana**

5. Which horse won the Derby, St Leger and 2000 Guineas in 1970? **Nijinsky**

6. Which literary character's main opponent was Von Stalhein? **Biggles'**

7. Who married the Earl of Bothwell in 1567? **Mary, Queen of Scots**

8. Which proboscis has 40,000 muscles? **An elephant's trunk**

9. Which American developed a talent as a great short-story writer while serving time in prison for embezzlement? **O Henry**

10. Which Tolstoy heroine threw herself under a train? **Anna Karenina**

11. In medieval art, what did a dog signify? Was it ferocity, fidelity or friendship? **Fidelity**

12. Whose last words, allegedly, were "I've had 18 straight whiskies, I think that's a record."? **Dylan Thomas'**

13. Which British poet is revered as a hero in Greece? **Byron**

14. True or false: a normal piano has 88 keys? **True**

15. Name one of the two bridges under which the crews pass in the University Boat Race? **Hammersmith or Barnes**

16. A size 9 man's shoe in Britain is what in the USA? **9½**

17. In mythology, who blinded Polyphemus? **Ulysses**

18. Which Psalm's first line is: "The Lord is my shepherd, I shall not want."? **Psalm 23**

19. What does a philogynist like? **Women**

20. Who had a No 1 hit in 1981 with *Tainted Love*? **Soft Cell**

Quiz 75

1. Which island merged with Tanganyika to form a new country in 1964? **Zanzibar**

2. Who became British Prime Minister in 1945? **Clement Attlee**

3. On TV, who presented *This Is Your Life* in 1995? **Michael Aspel**

4. Which Frenchman created the character of Monsieur Hulot? **Jacques Tati**

5. In the Tarzan novels, what does 'Tarzan' mean? Is it Ape Man, White Skin or Jungle King? **White Skin**

6. Which singer's catchphrase was "You ain't heard nothing yet."? **Al Jolson's**

7. Which Republic currently exists in France? **The Fifth**

8. Tupamaros are guerillas in which country? Is it Brazil, Chile or Uruguay? **Uruguay**

9. Which one word fits these definitions: sensitive or delicate, offer or present, and easily chewed? **Tender**

10. Who wrote the songs *Jambalaya, Your Cheating Heart, Hey, Good Lookin'* and *Cold Cold Heart*? **Hank Williams**

11. If you sailed west from Land's End and followed the same line of latitude, which country would you reach first? **Canada**

12. After India became independent, dispute over which state led to a war with Pakistan? **Kashmir**

13. What would you do with kvass? Would you eat it, drink it or paint it? **Drink it**

14. Who was Olympic Men's 400 Metres champion in 1992? **Quincy Watts**

15. What nationality was the artist Albrecht Dürer? Was he Belgian, Dutch or German? **German**

16. The Menin Gate is a memorial for British soldiers who fell in which battle? **Ypres**

17. Why was 29 a fateful number for Mrs Beeton, Anne Boleyn, Carole Landis and Percy Shelley? **All died aged 29**

18. From which country did Israeli commandoes rescue 106 hijacked air passengers in 1976? Was it Lebanon, Egypt or Uganda? **Uganda**

19. What was Christopher Dean's job before he became a professional skater? **Policeman**

20. In which sport would you go to a basho? **Sumo wrestling**

Quiz 76

1. Who, in films, played Hans Christian Andersen and the trumpeter Red Nicholls? **Danny Kaye**

2. What does the prefix 'crypto' mean? **Secret, unknown**

3. Which country's international car registration letters are PL? **Poland's**

4. Who played Ada in *For the Love of Ada*? **Irene Handl**

5. Where would you find a daglock? In a canal, on a sheep's rear end or in a safe? **Sheep's rear end (dirt covered clump of wool)**

6. How many years of marriage are indicated by a china wedding anniversary? **20**

7. How many decibels is the average whisper? Is it 5, 10 or 20? **20**

8. Which gangster was shot dead by the FBI on 22nd July 1934 as he came out of the Biograph Cinema in Chicago? **John Dillinger**

9. Who wrote *To the Lighthouse* and *Mrs Dalloway*? **Virginia Woolf**

10. Who captained Spurs when they did the double in 1961? **Danny Blanchflower**

11. What is the legal name for a spoken or written insult against religious belief or sacred objects? **Blasphemy**

12. True or false: a cord is a measure of cut wood? **True**

13. What was Bing Crosby's first name? **Harry**

14. Which Irish novelist was unable to walk or stand until he was 17, and then became an outstanding athlete and footballer at Dublin University? **Bram Stoker**

15. What was banned in the USA by the 18th Amendment? **Alcohol**

16. Where are the BBC gardens? **Barnsdale**

17. Which famous American folksinger had the first names Woodrow Wilson? **Woody Guthrie**

18. Which Canadian city was devastated in 1917 when an ammunition ship blew up in the harbour? **Halifax**

19. In which country did the 1976 Jonestown massacre occur? Was it Guyana, USA or Guatemala? **Guyana**

20. Which is the largest city in China? **Shanghai**

Quiz 77

1. The eight month period known as The Reign of Terror occurred during which 18th century upheaval? **French Revolution**

2. At what interval is the Passion Play performed in Oberammagau? **Every 10 years**

3. In which US state did Geronimo carry out his marauding? **Arizona**

4. In the 18th century, what was sold by shops which advertised 'drunk for a penny; dead drunk for tuppence'? **Gin**

5. Who starred in the silent films *Intolerance*, *Broken Blossoms* and *Orphans of the Storm*? **Lilian Gish**

6. Members of which clan were massacred in Glencoe in 1692? **MacDonalds**

7. In what field would the terms echinus, fusarole and abacus be used? **Architecture**

8. Whose followers in fashion formed 'The Club of the Fringed Glove'? **Beau Brummel's**

9. The Castle, The Giantess and The Beehive are all found in Yellowstone Park. What are they? **Geysers**

10. Which German said in 1936: "Guns will make us powerful: butter will only make us fat."? **Hermann Goering**

11. In his generation Leon Goossens was considered the finest performer on which instrument? **Oboe**

12. What did the W stand for in film director D W Griffith's name? **Wark**

13. What kind of creature is a flying fox? **Bat**

14. Which group in the 1960s had Top Ten hits with *Yes I Will*, *Sorry Suzanne* and *We're Through*? **The Hollies**

15. Which American tree, whose wood is considered good for hammers, mallets, etc., has varieties called pignut, mockernut and king nut? **Hickory**

16. What was the name of Lenny Henry's character in *Chef*? **Gareth Blackstock**

17. What does the koala bear eat? **Eucalyptus leaves**

18. Who was Commander-in-Chief of the Parliamentary forces in the English Civil War? **Thomas Fairfax**

19. John Huston's film *The Dead* was based on a story by whom? **James Joyce**

20. Who lived on Inner Farne Island as a hermit from 677 to 684 AD? **St Cuthbert**

Quiz 78

1. Who led the junta which seized the Falklands in 1982? **Galtieri**

2. In which county is Romney Marsh? **Kent**

3. On which island is Mount Suribachi? **Iwo Jima**

4. Who played King Feisal of Iraq in the film *Lawrence of Arabia*? **Alec Guinness**

5. Which bandleader married Lana Turner and Ava Gardner? Was it Stan Kenton, Woody Herman or Artie Shaw? **Artie Shaw**

6. Which planet has satellites called Miranda, Ariel, Puck and Desdemona? **Uranus**

7. During World War 2 Norman Shelley was enlisted to imitate whom in radio broadcasts? **Winston Churchill**

8. Which Englishman was murdered outside the Dakota Building in New York in 1980? **John Lennon**

9. True or false: Italy joined the EEC in 1958? **True**

10. Which doctor performed the first human heart transplant? **Christiaan Barnard**

11. What was the subject of the 1963 Beeching Report? **Railways**

12. Who wrote *The Forsyte Saga*? **John Galsworthy**

13. Who played Sir Lancelot Spratt in the *Doctor* films? **James Robertson Justice**

14. Who painted the famous picture of Guernica, bombed in the Spanish civil war? **Picasso**

15. Which MP said: "I married beneath me – all women do."? **Nancy Astor**

16. In Russia, what was a gulag? **Prison camp**

17. Name Reg Holdsworth's mother-in-law. **Maud Grimes**

18. What is the correct collective name for a litter of piglets? **Farrow**

19. The adjective 'costal' applies to which part of the body? **Ribs**

20. Phnom Penh is capital of which country? **Cambodia**

Quiz 79

1. Which Irish tenor was so admired and respected that he was made a Papal count? **John McCormack**

2. In which city are the US football team The Redskins based? **Washington**

3. What colour flag is flown at beaches deemed clean and pollution free? **Blue**

4. What is the capital of New Zealand? **Wellington**

5. Which film family were introduced in the 1947 film *Holiday Camp*? **The Huggetts**

6. Which judge presided at the infamous Bloody Assizes in 1685? **Judge Jeffreys**

7. Which one word means a poultry disease, a fruit's seed and a spot on a die? **Pip**

8. Which famous literary duo first appeared together in the story *The Man with Two Left Feet*? **Bertie Wooster and Jeeves**

9. What is the positive heavy particle of an atom's nucleus? Is it the proton, neutron or electron? **Proton**

10. In which sport did Phil Read win many World Championships? **Motor Cycling**

11. Which TV series featured Lord and Lady Brightlingsea, Lord Seadown and Helmsley Thwaite? ***The Buccaneers***

12. What is the correct name for larceny from a consecrated building? **Sacrilege**

13. Which country's king was the Prisoner of Zenda? **Ruritania's**

14. Who would use a trochee? A poet, a surgeon or an engineer? **A poet**

15. Of what did Prince Albert die? **Typhoid fever**

16. What would you do with a zinfandel? Wear it, play it or make wine with it? **Make wine**

17. What is British Honduras now called? **Belize**

18. True or false: the largest island in Asia is Sumatra? **False (Borneo)**

19. Ipoh, Kuching, Johore Bahru and Georgetown are all towns in which Commonwealth country? **Malaysia**

20. What nationality was Boutros Boutros Ghali, Secretary General of the UN? **Egyptian**

Quiz 80

1. The French ship *Petit Pierre* was the first to be driven (in 1902) by what? Was it a propellor, a diesel engine or a steam turbine? **Diesel engine**

2. In what field did Walter Gropius achieve fame? **Architecture**

3. For what is the Prix Goncourt awarded? Is it music, cinema or literature? **Literature**

4. In what year was Lord Mountbatten murdered? Was it 1977, 1978 or 1979? **1979**

5. In which game would you use the expression 'J'adoube'? **Chess**

6. By what name did Rose Louise Hovick achieve fame? **Gypsy Rose Lee**

7. What is the currency of Argentina? **Peso**

8. In films, who played Captain Bligh, Henry VIII and Quasimodo? **Charles Laughton**

9. Who was the first Prime Minister of Israel? **David Ben-Gurion**

10. Of which country was Ferdinand Marcos President from 1965 to 1986? **Philippines**

11. In Russia, what is Kyzyl Kum? Is it a gigantic crater, a huge lake or a desert? **Desert**

12. Who landed at Le Bourget airport on May 21st, 1927? **Charles Lindbergh**

13. Which country has Colombia to the west and Guyana to the east? **Venezuela**

14. True or false: China is the world's top fishing nation (in tonnage)? **True**

15. Which famous English comedy star was born blind but gained his sight after a fit of coughing? **George Formby**

16. In which country do the Walloons live? **Belgium**

17. For what sort of activity was Sir Francis Walsingham, Elizabeth I's Secretary of State, best remembered? **Espionage**

18. Which musical note has half the value of a crotchet? **Quaver**

19. Which sport is believed to have originated on Pentecost Island as an initiation ceremony? **Bungee Jumping**

20. Which word is used in radio call signs for Y? **Yankee**

Quiz 81

1. With which identification system is Francis Galton associated? **Fingerprints**

2. Where was Joan of Arc burnt at the stake? **Rouen**

3. What does etymology deal with? **Word origins**

4. Who played Ratso Rizzo in the film *Midnight Cowboy*? **Dustin Hoffman**

5. Who is reckoned to have invented bifocal lenses? **Benjamin Franklin**

6. In which daily newspaper does Rupert the Bear appear? ***Daily Express***

7. What colour is puce? Is it orange yellow, purple brown or light red? **Purple Brown**

8. Where did the Confederates surrender in 1865? Was it Gettysburg, Richmond or Appomattox?
Appomattox

9. On TV, what one word connects these characters? Martin Platt, Kate Wilson and Gladys Emmanuel?
Nurse

10. True or false: the Yucatan Peninsula is in Honduras? **False (Mainly in Mexico.)**

11. Who plays Jean-Luc Picard in *Star Trek – The Next Generation*? **Patrick Stewart**

12. In which film did John Wayne use a group of boys on a cattle drive? ***The Cowboys***

13. Who succeeded Henry VIII as monarch? **Edward VI**

14. Which Spanish artist's most famous painting was *The Persistence of Memory*? **Dali's**

15. In which country was Alfredo di Stefano of Real Madrid born? Was it Argentina, Spain, or Colombia? **Argentina**

16. What name is given to a joint of beef cut from the breast next to the ribs? **Brisket**

17. In which US state are The Everglades? **Florida**

18. What would you do with a filibeg? Play it, fight with it or wear it? **Wear it**

19. In which sea are the Dodecanese Islands? **Aegean Sea**

20. In what year was the first decimal coin circulated in Britain? **1969**

Quiz 82

1. From which planet does Dr Who come? **Gallifrey**
2. In 1994 the Chinese sporting World Champions Lu Bin and Yang Aihua tested positive for drugs. In what sport were they world champions? **Swimming**
3. Who wrote *Dr Zhivago*? **Boris Pasternak**
4. Which swashbuckling star starred in the silent films *The Three Musketeers*, *Robin Hood* and *The Black Pirate*? **Douglas Fairbanks**
5. Which one word can mean a parasitic worm, the hook of an anchor and a lucky chance? **Fluke**
6. True or false: the organisation RIBA is for architects? **True**
7. What is measured in bathyl, abyssal and hadal zones? Is it the density of stars, mountain crevasses or ocean depths? **Ocean depths**
8. Which is the world's oldest stock exchange? Is it Antwerp, Hamburg or Amsterdam? **Antwerp**
9. True or false: Georgetown is the capital of Barbados? **False (It's Bridgetown.)**
10. On TV, whose stooges have included Rodney Bewes, Derek Fowlds and Roy North? **Basil Brush's**
11. Who played Tommy Steele in the film *The Tommy Steele Story*? **Tommy Steele**
12. Who was Wimbledon Women's Singles Champion in 1994? **Conchita Martinez**

13. In Jewish folklore, who is Lilith? **A Demon or Adam's first wife**

14. What does a myologist study? Is it fungi, muscles or mosses? **Muscles**

15. Which performer was shown on the Ed Sullivan Show only from the waist up? **Elvis Presley**

16. Who wrote *All Quiet On the Western Front*? **Erich Remarque**

17. Which is the world's largest computer manufacturer? **IBM**

18. Which detective was helped by Steve? **Paul Temple**

19. Which animal caused the death of William III? **Mole**

20. From which musical does the song *Goodbye* come? ***White Horse Inn***

Quiz 83

1. In the story *The Final Problem*, who fell to his death at the Reichenbach Falls? **Professor Moriarty**

2. Who was the founder of the Jewish priesthood? **Aaron**

3. Who crossed Niagara Falls on a tightrope in 1859? **Charles Blondin**

4. In Old English what did 'acre' mean? **Field**

5. When Victoria became queen, who ceased to be queen? **Adelaide**

6. In films, which duo met Capt Kidd, Dr Jekyll and Mr Hyde, Frankenstein, the Mummy and the Invisible Man? **Abbot and Costello**

7. On which river does Ely stand? **The Ouse**

8. Which disease is caused by the fungus *Ceratostomella Ulmi*? **Dutch Elm disease**

9. Who was the mother of Elizabeth I? **Anne Boleyn**

10. Who wrote *Silas Marner*, *Adam Bede* and *Daniel Deronda*? **George Eliot**

11. In North America it is the moose. What is it in Eurasia? **Elk**

12. How many Oscars did Richard Burton win? **None**

13. Which famous American was known as The Wizard of Menlo Park? **Thomas Edison**

14. Which famous leader officially brought an end to the Pharaonic era in Egypt? **Alexander the Great**

15. What are barristers called in Scotland? **Advocates**

16. Who teamed up with Peter Gabriel for the Top Ten hit *Don't Give Up* in 1986? **Kate Bush**

17. Which 'magic' word was written on amulets in the form of an equilateral triangle? **Abracadabra**

18. Who is believed to be the author of the Acts of the Apostles? **St Luke**

19. In which island country is Adam's Peak? **Sri Lanka**

20. Who allegedly said: "There's a sucker born every minute."? **P T Barnum**

Quiz 84

1. Who wrote the *Whiteoak* family series? **Mazo De La Roche**

2. Who led a mission from Rome to King Ethelbert in 587 AD? **St Augustine**

3. Who directed the films *It Happened One Night*, *Mr Deeds Goes To Town* and *You Can't Take It With You*? **Frank Capra**

4. Who had a No 2 hit in 1966 with *I Can't Control Myself*? **The Troggs**

5. What stands in the Sacred Tank in Amritsar in India? **The Golden Temple**

6. Who painted *The Anatomy Lesson of Dr Tulip* in 1632? **Rembrandt**

7. Admiralty, kedge, grapnel, sheet and bower are all types of what? **Anchor**

8. In Greek mythology, where did the nymphs, the Dryads, live? **In trees**

9. For what is the Italian town of Carrara famous? **(White) Marble**

10. Which element, not found freely in nature, was discovered in 1669 by distilling a mixture of urine and charcoal? **Phosphorus**

11. Which silent film star was known as America's Sweetheart? **Mary Pickford**

12. Which plant, sought everywhere, has a flower known as the 'poor man's weather-glass'? **Scarlet Pimpernel**

13. What name is given to the alloy of copper and zinc that resembles gold? **Pinchbeck**

14. What was the sequel to *Little Women*? ***Good Wives***

15. What branch of science was known until 1603 as 'earth-lore'? **Geology**

16. To what use did an alchemist put an alembic? **Distilling liquids**

17. As a mark of his achievements in North Africa, what title did Earl Alexander take? **Alexander of Tunis**

18. Against whom were Cicero's speeches, the Philippics, directed? **Mark Antony**

19. Which ore produces aluminium? **Bauxite**

20. Which famous American statesman and scientist said: "There never was a good war, nor a bad peace."? **Benjamin Franklin**

Quiz 85

1. Is a dhole a wild dog, a crocodile, or a songbird? **Wild Dog**

2. Which is the second smallest state in the US? **Delaware**

3. What is the date of the Feast of All Saints? **November 1st**

4. Which kind of tree mainly produced the fossilised resin that becomes amber? **Pine**

5. Who wrote the play *A Taste of Honey*? **Shelagh Delaney**

6. Which was the first war of which there are photographic records? **Crimean**

7. In the TV series *Hi De Hi*, who was the never seen but much heard of supervisor of the chalet maids? **Miss Cathcart**

8. Oliver Cromwell's enemies accused him of decadence because he excelled in two sports. Name one. **Cricket or wrestling**

9. In which American state is Death Valley? **California**

10. Which European country was ruled by Harold Bluetooth until 988 AD? **Denmark**

11. Which disease does the Wasserman Test diagnose? **Syphilis**

12. Name the dog which appeared on the HMV record label. **Nipper**

13. Under what name did actress Maria Magdalena von Losch become famous? **Marlene Dietrich**

14. Which country won the gold medal for soccer in the 1996 Olympics? **Nigeria**

15. Who was the father of James I of England? **Lord Darnley**

16. What is the French equivalent of Italy's Giro D'Italia? **Tour De France**

17. Whose successor is a baby boy born at the precise moment of the title holder's death? **Dalai Lama**

18. Abraham Darby designed and built the world's first what? **Iron bridge**

19. What is the other name of Deadly Nightshade? **Belladonna**

20. What is the first event in the Decathlon? **100 metres**

Quiz 86

1. Near which British seaside resort are the Great and Little Ormes? **Llandudno**

2. Which pop group named itself after a 1956 John Wayne film? **The Searchers**

3. Which plant's Latin name is *Ficus Elastica*? Is it the rubber plant, aspidistra or ivy? **Rubber plant**

4. In World War 2 what name was given to the German technique of sending U-Boats out in groups? **Wolf Pack**

5. True or false: Muslims have to pray 7 times a day? **False (5 times)**

6. Kohoutek, Tempel-Tuttle and Halley's are all what? **Comets**

7. The Chinese call it the Huang Ho. What do we call it? **Yellow River**

8. The 1984 TV drama *Threads* showed a nuclear bomb falling on which British city? **Sheffield**

9. What calibre should a firearm be to be classed as artillery? Over 10mm, 20mm or 30mm? **Over 20mm**

10. Who married Bianca de Macias on 12th May 1971? **Mick Jagger**

11. What is a bullace? Is it a fruit, a fish or a bird? **Fruit**

12. Where in Britain is the Neolithic village of Skara Brae? **The Orkneys**

13. What is the other name for the snow leopard? **The ounce**

14. The battle of Vittoria in 1813 was the last battle in which war? **Peninsular War**

15. Into which sea does the River Jordan flow? Is it the Mediterranean, the Red or the Dead? **The Dead Sea**

16. Which group had hits with *Mr Tambourine Man* and *Eight Miles High*? **The Byrds**

17. Who played Philo Beddoe in two films? **Clint Eastwood**

18. Which Mexican revolutionary, first name Emiliano, was assassinated in 1919? **Zapata**

19. Which singer was given the nickname The Killer? **Jerry Lee Lewis**

20. Which is South Africa's *administrative* capital: Cape Town, Bloemfontein or Pretoria? **Pretoria**

Quiz 87

1. True or false: George Washington was a surveyor before becoming a soldier? **True**

2. Who played Ironside on TV? **Raymond Burr**

3. To a sailor especially, what is a hawser? **A rope**

4. Which kingdom was ruled by Herod the Great? **Judaea**

5. What was the profession of John Dunlop, who patented the pneumatic tyre in 1888? Was he a cart maker, an accountant or a veterinary surgeon? **Veterinary surgeon**

6. What did Jason and the Argonauts seek? **The Golden Fleece**

7. What name is shared by an Asian capital, a Canadian provincial capital and an African lake? **Victoria**

8. During prohibition, what name was given to an illegal drinking club? **Speakeasy**

9. Which river is formed east of Boroughbridge by the confluence of the Swale and the Ure rivers? **River Ouse**

10. What was the name of Richard Beckinsale's character in *Porridge*? **Lennie Godber**

11. In which sport were Tramontona British Champions from 1986 to 1989? (Black Bears and Hildon have been more recent winners.) **Polo**

12. Which people's name means "eaters of raw meat"? **Eskimoes**

13. Who played The Forger in the film *The Great Escape*? **Donald Pleasence**

14. Who wrote *The Sea Wolf* and *White Fang*? **Jack London**

15. With what is a thanatologist concerned? Is it death, the sea or hidden treasure? **Death**

16. Which animal is sometimes said to be 'in velvet'? **Deer**

17. True or false: *The Two Towers* is a book in *The Lord of the Rings* trilogy? **True**

18. Which leader wrote his thoughts in a little red book? **Chairman Mao**

19. In 1707, which English admiral was thrown ashore when his flagship, *Association*, sank off the Scilly Isles, and was murdered by a woman for the great ring on his finger? **Cloudesley Shovell**

20. Which word, derived from Polynesian, means forbidden or prohibited? **Taboo**

Quiz 88

1. Who was Olympic Boxing Light Heavyweight Gold medallist in 1960? **Cassius Clay**

2. Tau, omicron, epsilon and lambda are all found where? **In the Greek alphabet**

3. The discovery of the Babington Plot led to the death of which monarch? **Mary, Queen of Scots**

4. In which country are Europe's only wild bison? **Poland**

5. Which mythical creature was the symbol of virginity? **Unicorn**

6. In which film is this the last line: "Tomorrow is another day."? ***Gone With the Wind***

7. Which ex-England goalkeeper was killed in the Munich air crash? **Frank Swift**

8. Which monkeys are known for their blue and red faces and buttocks? **Mandrills**

9. Who played the female lead in the *Ghostbusters* films? **Sigourney Weaver**

10. What was the name of King Arthur's treacherous nephew? **Mordred or (Modred)**

11. Which animal lives in a citadel? Is it a weasel, a mole or a badger? **Mole**

12. Which group released an album called *Lexicon of Love*? **ABC**

13. True or false: Paul Newman's wife is Joanne Dru? **False (It is Joanne Woodward.)**

14. On TV, which holiday camp featured in the series *Hi De Hi*? **Maplins**

15. In which war was the Battle of Antietam? **American Civil War**

16. Which Labour weekly did Michael Foot edit for nine years? ***Tribune***

17. Rulers of which ancient civilisation wore a double crown to signify the unification of the Upper and Lower kingdoms? **Egypt**

18. Which was the first British pop group to tour China? **Wham**

19. F Murray Abraham won Best Actor Oscar for his part in which musical biographical film? ***Amadeus***

20. Of what is petrology the study? **Rocks**

Quiz 89

1. Who founded the National Viewers and Listeners Association? **Mary Whitehouse**

2. Imran Khan played cricket for Worcestershire and which other English county? **Sussex**

3. Where are calderas found? On the sea bed, in kitchens or on the tops of volcanoes? **On the tops of volcanoes**

4. Which character appears in the most Shakespeare plays? **Falstaff**

5. In which sport did Richard Meade win Olympic gold? **Equestrianism – 3 day event**

6. Which common object has an inertia reel? **Car seat belt**

7. What name is given to a cow's first milk after calving? Is it bedew, bennets, or beestings? **Beestings**

8. Name one of Britain's allies in The Seven Years War. **Prussia or Hanover**

9. True or false: Nicolas Soult was one of Napoleon's generals? **True**

10. What number do the Roman numerals MDXCV represent? **1595**

11. Which comedian and *That's Life* presenter was famous for his odd odes? **Cyril Fletcher**

12. What character did Paul Eddington play in *Yes, Minister*? **Jim Hacker**

13. In one word, what is yeast? **(A) Fungus**

14. Who described foxhunting as "the unspeakable in pursuit of the uneatable."? **Oscar Wilde**

15. In London, what was the Tyburn? A stream, the gallows or an arch? **A stream**

16. The Cod Wars of the 1970s were between Britain and which country? **Iceland**

17. In Norse mythology, who was the evil and mischievous god? **Loki**

18. Who killed Macbeth in Shakespeare's play? **Macduff**

19. Which is the loudest insect? Is it a cricket, a cicada or a blow fly? **Cicada**

20. For what purpose did the Mayan people build pyramids? Was it as tombs, temples or palaces? **Temples**

Quiz 90

1. Who was detective Sexton Blake's assistant? **Tinker**

2. Where would you be if you ate al fresco? **Outside, in the open air**

3. Who lost the battle of Ulm in 1805? Was it Prussia, Austria or Russia? **Austria**

4. What is the plural of axis? **Axes**

5. True or false: Melbourne is the state capital of Victoria? **True**

6. Who is the leading character of the story that has a fairy called Tinker Bell? **Peter Pan**

7. What word is used to describe descending a sheer face by sliding down a doubled rope? **Abseiling**

8. What was found buried at Sutton Hoo in 1939? **A Saxon ship**

9. Which magical character was played by Gudrun Ure on TV in 1985? **Supergran**

10. On which river does Belfast stand? Is it the Liffey, Lagan or Lough? **Lagan**

11. In which US state are the Green Mountains? **Vermont**

12. Which physical property allows a needle to float on water? **Surface tension**

13. Which one word means a type of sandpiper, an Elizabethan collar and to trump at cards? **Ruff**

14. Which common substance is made by boiling down horns, hides and hoofs? **Glue**

15. Who won Best Actor Oscar in 1989 for *My Left Foot*? **Daniel Day-Lewis**

16. If your face was rugose, what would it be? **Wrinkled**

17. What type of music is produced by French speaking settlers of Louisiana? **Cajun**

18. In Arthurian legend, what was Ron? Was it Arthur's spear, shield or horse? **Spear**

19. In which country was the governor or viceroy called The Khedive from 1867 to 1914? **Egypt**

20. If you carry out bel canto, what are you doing? **Singing**

Quiz 91

1. True or false: Lionel Hampton played the tenor saxophone? **False (He played the vibraphone.)**
2. In which county is the naval base of Gosport? **Hampshire**
3. Who played the camp commandant in the TV series *Colditz*? **Bernard Hepton**
4. Who said about sex: "The whole thing is like finding a frog in a coffee jar."? **Stephen Fry**
5. What part of your body would interest a rhinologist? **Nose**
6. Which country lies between Zimbabwe and the sea? **Mozambique**
7. Which 'ruler' died of a "bastard tertian ague" in 1658 and later his body was mistreated? **Oliver Cromwell**
8. What pachydermic nickname is given to a gift or possession which is useless and expensive to maintain? **White Elephant**
9. Which bird is used in a squab pie? **Pigeon**
10. What is grown in a paddy field? **Rice**
11. Red, fennec, Arctic and bat-eared are all species of which animal? **Fox**
12. Spell DESICCATED. **DESICCATED**

13. In what game could you have a pone: Mah Jong, backgammon or cards? **Cards (Player to right of dealer who cuts the cards.)**

14. Which Government Department is responsible for broadcasting and the media, the arts, sport and recreation? **National Heritage**

15. The ancient figure called a fylfot or gammadion became better and more threateningly known to us as what? **Swastika**

16. What was the name of the butler in the TV series *To the Manor Born*? **Brabinger**

17. Truc or false: a futtock is a ship's timber? **True**

18. In a famous Beckett play, for whom were Vladimir and Estragon waiting? **Godot**

19. From which country did Paddington Bear come? **Peru**

20. Which new watersport was added to the Olympics in 1984? **Synchronised swimming**

Quiz 92

1. In which popular TV series did a character called Seymour Atterthwaite appear for one series? ***Last of the Summer Wine***

2. Which word means to turn a ship on one side for cleaning and caulking? **Careening**

3. In the famous poem, who stole the green eye of the little yellow god? **Mad Carew**

4. Where in London is the American Embassy? **Grosvenor Square**

5. Which Danish player played for Newcastle United when they won the Fairs Cup? **Ben Arentoft**

6. In which film did Robert Redford and Jane Fonda play newly weds who lived on the top floor of a liftless apartment building? ***Barefoot In the Park***

7. What name was given to the programme of social reform attempted by President Truman? **Fair Deal**

8. What name in the Bible means 'He who strives with God' and was the name given to Jacob after he'd wrestled with an angel? **Israel**

9. What is the supreme goal of Buddhists? **Nirvana**

10. Which country issued a 12d black stamp in 1851? Was it Britain, Australia or Canada? **Canada**

11. With which ancient people would you associate *The Book of the Dead*? **Egyptians**

12. If you suffer from comedones, what have you got? **Blackheads**

13. From which film did Stevie Wonder's *I Just Called To Say I Love You* come? ***The Woman in Red***

14. Who wrote the novel *Fair Stood the Wind For France*? **H E Bates**

15. Which magazine was launched by the BBC in 1929? ***The Listener***

16. In which sport did Wilt Chamberlain and Alton Byrd achieve fame? **Basketball**

17. Which group would you associate with *Light My Fire*, *Hello I Love You* and *Riders On the Storm*?
The Doors

18. Who was *The Once and Future King* written about by T H White? **King Arthur**

19. What do you use if you foretell the future by conchomancy? **Shells**

20. Who was the first presenter of TV's *Tomorrow's World*? **Raymond Baxter**

Quiz 93

1. Who was described as 'the mouse that built an empire'? **Mickey Mouse**

2. What is the Church of England's smallest administrative unit? **A parish**

3. Who played John in the TV series *Dear John*?
Ralph Bates

4. What was Marilyn Monroe's character name in *Some Like It Hot*? **Sugar Kane**

5. Who, in a famous monologue by Stanley Holloway, was swallowed by a lion at Blackpool Zoo? Was it Sam, Albert or Charley? **Albert**

6. Which people's creation legend is told in the Dreamtime Stories? **Australian Aborigines'**

7. Who put Sweeney Todd's victims into her pies?
Mrs Lovett

8. Which pop group released the albums *White Light, White Heat* and *Loaded*? **Velvet Underground**

9. The adjective 'cutaneous' refers to which part of the body? Is it the nails, the blood vessels or the skin? **Skin**

10. In films, who played the Thin Man? **William Powell**

11. Where in Britain did the Battle of the Beanfield occur in 1985? **Stonehenge**

12. What is added to mineral water to make tonic water? **Quinine**

13. What first ran from Paddington to Farringdon Street in 1863? **London Underground**

14. What is the collective name for a group of mice? **Nest**

15. In the nursery rhyme, what would be Curly Locks' only work? **To sew a fine seam**

16. True or false: the *Torrey Canyon* was a Kuwaiti oil tanker? **True**

17. Who wrote the book : *Mussolini: His Part in My Downfall*? **Spike Milligan**

18. In which county was John Major's constituency in the 1992 General Election? **Cambridgeshire**

19. What was called the jewel in Queen Victoria's crown? **India**

20. Which plant was believed to shriek when pulled up? **Mandrake**

Quiz 94

1. What is pargeting? Is it a system of roof tiling, glazed porcelain or a type of plastering? **A type of plastering**

2. Who played Ingrid Bergman's husband in *Casablanca*? **Paul Henreid**

3. If you had a gigot would you play it, eat it or wear it? **Eat it**

4. Which cereal is used in Scotch Broth? **Barley**

5. Who had Top Ten hits in the 1980s with *Wouldn't It Be Good*, *The Riddle* and *Wide Boy*? **Nik Kershaw**

6. Which islands did Captain Cook name the Friendly Islands? **Tonga**

7. Which TV series featured the *Daily Crucible* newspaper? ***Hot Metal***

8. How many unions merged to form Unison in 1993? Was it 3, 4 or 5? **3**

9. Which story and film were inspired by a World War 2 shipwreck off the island of Barra? ***Whisky Galore***

10. Matlock is the administrative centre of which county? **Derbyshire**

11. Who was head of the German SS? **Himmler**

12. True or false: Anthony Trollope wrote *Tom Brown's Schooldays*? **False (Thomas Hughes did.)**

13. Which holes at deck level in a ship's sides let water drain away? **Scuppers**

14. In which radio series did Osric Pureheart appear? ***Crazy People* (and *The Goon Show*)**

15. Who composed *Putting on the Ritz*, *Easter Parade* and *God Bless America*? **Irving Berlin**

16. Who founded the Free Presbyterian Church of Ulster in 1951? **Ian Paisley**

17. Blue Vinney is a type of what? Is it quartz, cheese or moss? **Cheese**

18. Which ex-soldier wrote *The Seven Pillars of Wisdom*? **T E Lawrence (Lawrence of Arabia)**

19. Who was Russian Foreign Minister from 1957 to 1985? **Gromyko**

20. Who appeared in these films: *From Here To Eternity*, *Suddenly Last Summer*, *Red River* and *The Misfits*? **Montgomery Clift**

Quiz 95

1. Who played The Virginian on TV? **James Drury**

2. When were Nobel Prizes first awarded? Was it 1901, 1905 or 1909? **1901**

3. What are auctioned at Tattersalls? **Racehorses**

4. Who was the youngest general in the American Civil War? **George A Custer**

5. With which sporting or leisure activity was Edward Whymper associated? **Mountaineering**

6. Which musical includes the songs *Gee, Officer Krupke* and *America*? ***West Side Story***

7. Who, on TV, presented the Arts programme *Monitor* and was Director General of BBC TV from 1968 to 1975? **Huw Wheldon**

8. True or false: film star Ray Milland was born in Wales? **True**

9. Who played Glenn Miller's wife in the film *The Glenn Miller Story*? **June Allyson**

10. Is a passepied a hopping bird, a dance or a type of slipper? **A dance**

11. Which organisation's motto is "Courtesy and Care"? **The Automobile Association's**

12. Which controversial Oliver Stone film starred Woody Harrelson as Mickey? ***Natural Born Killers***

13. For what was John Singer Sargent famous? Was he a painter, writer or composer? **Painter**

14. Who won the Nobel Prize for chemistry the year after Marie Curie died? Was it her husband, her daughter or her son? **Her daughter**

15. Which legendary ship is doomed to sail forever? **The *Flying Dutchman***

16. Which cartoonist created St Trinian's? **Ronald Searle**

17. What sort of music did Ira D Sankey compose? **Hymns**

18. Which English city is named after Snot and his tribe? **Nottingham**

19. Who wrote the *Gormenghast Trilogy*? **Mervyn Peake**

20. "A day that shall live in infamy." What is the exact date of that day? **7th December 1941 (The Japanese attack on Pearl Harbor.)**

Quiz 96

1. In what year was Princess Margaret married? Was it 1959, 1960 or 1963? **1960**

2. Which TV sexy serial featured a model called Sugar Bush? ***Black Eyes***

3. Which inventor's first film (one minute long) was called *Fred Ott's Sneeze*? **Edison's**

4. True or false: Harold Macmillan met Ian Smith on board HMS *Tiger* in 1966? **False (Harold Wilson did.)**

5. Which country's soldiers might wear a stiff skirt called a fustanella? **Greece's**

6. Who was the last English king to die in battle? **Richard III**

7. Who starred in the silent films *Blood and Sand*, *The Eagle* and *The Sheik*? **Rudolph Valentino**

8. Which is the ancestral home of the Dukes of Bedford? **Woburn Abbey**

9. What was Tom's job in *The Water Babies*? **Chimney Sweep**

10. Alchemists sought for an object that would turn base metals into gold. What did they call this imaginary object? **Philosopher's Stone**

11. Who is the mother of James Ogilvy? **Princess Alexandra**

12. Which film star published his autobiography in three volumes, including *Snakes and Ladders* and *Orderly Man*? **Dirk Bogarde**

13. Which cartoon character was 'the fastest mouse in all Mexico'? **Speedy Gonzales**

14. Who could only play one tune – *Over the hills and far away*? **Tom, the piper's son**

15. Which African president was assassinated at a military review in 1981? **President Sadat of Egypt**

16. What has a testatrix done? **Made a will**

17. What is the popular name for toxaemia? **Blood poisoning**

18. In legend, what was the name of King Arthur's fairy sister? **Morgan Le Fay**

19. Which sci-fi film featured three robots called Huey, Louie and Dewey? ***Silent Running***

20. Who said about oral contraception: "I asked this girl to sleep with me and she said 'No'."? **Woody Allen**

Quiz 97

1. Which shipwrecked sailor settled a war between King Bombo and King Little? **Gulliver**

2. Who was the father of the disciples James and John? **Zebedee**

3. Which county's motif is a standing bear next to a ragged staff? **Warwickshire's**

4. Whose four wives included Ann Howe and Miranda Quarry? **Peter Sellers'**

5. Which is the last of the year's four Quarter days? **Christmas Day**

6. Which terrier is the largest of the terrier breeds? **Airedale**

7. Which bear protected Mowgli in *The Jungle Book*? **Baloo**

8. Which comedian's catchphrase was "Can you hear me, Mother?"? **Sandy Powell's**

9. Where was the first British Grand Prix held in 1926? **Brooklands**

10. Which branch of mathematics deals with the relationship between the sides and angles of triangles? **Trigonometry**

11. Where does the Lutine Bell hang? **Lloyds of London**

12. Who played the central character in the film *The Loneliness of the Long Distance Runner*? **Tom Courtenay**

13. What is a turnstone? Is it an ore, a bird or a flower? **A bird**

14. Who wrote the plays *Bar Mitzvah Boy* and *Spend, Spend, Spend*? **Jack Rosenthal**

15. Which Trojan's story is told in the *Aeneid* by Virgil? **Aeneas'**

16. In a nursery rhyme, where would you go to see a fine lady with bells on her toes? **Banbury Cross**

17. What was the title of the first women's magazine, published in 1693? ***The Ladies' Mercury***

18. How many points does a compass have? **32**

19. In which 1984 film did Sean Connery return as James Bond after a thirteen year gap? ***Never Say Never Again***

20. What is the last event in the Decathlon? **1500 metres**

Quiz 98

1. What number was represented by H in the Ancient Greek number system? **100**

2. Which is the most northerly town in England? **Berwick-on-Tweed**

3. Sloes are the fruit of which shrub? **Blackthorn**

4. Which golfer, in 1930, won both the US and British Opens, and the US and British Amateur championships? **Bobby Jones**

5. Which cousin of George V was murdered? **Czar Nicholas II**

6. Two British ships were sunk off Malaya three days after Japan entered World War 2. One was the *Prince of Wales*. What was the other? **HMS *Repulse***

7. Where exactly would you find the books of Tobit, Judith and Baruch and the Epistle of Timothy? **In the *Apocrypha***

8. What is Paddy Ashdown's first name? **Jeremy**

9. What colour (excluding trim) is Thomas the Tank Engine? **Blue**

10. What did St Columba claim to have seen in the 6th century? **Loch Ness Monster**

11. Who played the title role in the 1968 film *The Girl On a Motorbike*? **Marianne Faithful**

12. In which 1930's musical, successfully revived in recent years, is Bill Snibson the central character? ***Me and My Girl***

13. In Jane Austen's *Pride and Prejudice*, whom does Elizabeth Bennet finally marry? **Mr Darcy**

14. What did John Walker invent and first call Congreves? **Friction matches**

15. Where would you find the Mount of Venus, the Mount of Mercury and the Mount of the Sun? **On your hand**

16. In medicine, what part of your body is treated by reflexology? **Soles of your feet**

17. Who was the most famous person to be born in Braunau Am Inn in Austria? **Adolf Hitler**

18. In which country did Karl Marx spend the last 34 years of his life? **England**

19. What is the cast-off skin of a snake called? **Slough**

20. Which is the only kingdom in Africa? **Morocco**

Quiz 99

1. Who played the lead in the films *The Square Peg*, *A Stitch in Time* and *Man of the Moment*? **Norman Wisdom**

2. Baron Temple of Mount Temple was British Prime Minister under which name? **Palmerston**

3. Which bird is also known as the windhover? **Kestrel**

4. What was the name of Charles Lindbergh's plane? ***Spirit of St Louis***

5. Name one of the two countries in which you would find Coptic Christians? **Egypt or Ethiopia**

6. Who was the first golfer to win the US Masters four times? **Arnold Palmer**

7. Who founded the Women's Social and Political Union in 1903? **Mrs Pankhurst**

8. Which African river was first explored by the Scottish surgeon, Mungo Park? **Niger**

9. Who beat Denis Law's record of goals scored in FA Cup matches? **Ian Rush**

10. What do Spaniards traditionally eat as the New Year begins? **Grapes**

11. Crested, Jackass, Fairy, and Black-Footed are all species of what? **Penguin**

12. Who became Prime Minister of France in 1940 at the age of 84? **Marshal Pétain**

13. Which alloy contains 90% tin, 8% copper and 2% antimony? **Pewter**

14. In which Australian state is Newcastle? **New South Wales**

15. Where exactly in North America would you find Goat Island? **Middle of Niagara Falls**

16. Who won Best Actress Oscar for her performance in *The Trip To Bountiful*? **Geraldine Page**

17. Which *ITMA* character used the catchphrase "It's being so cheerful as keeps me going!"? **Mona Lott**

18. Who would you find in a panopticon? **Prisoners (It is a prison.)**

19. In Disney's *The Sword In the Stone*, by what name is Arthur called until he withdraws the sword? **Wart**

20. In *Macbeth*, whose ghost appears at Macbeth's banquet? **Banquo's**

Quiz 100

1. What does a hippophobe fear? **Horses**

2. What is the collective name for a group of leopards? **A leap**

3. In the film *When Harry Met Sally*, who played Harry? **Billy Crystal**

4. Who played the radio talk-show host in TV's *Midnight Caller*? **Gary Cole**

5. Which one word fits these definitions: to transplant, bribery and hard work? **Graft**

6. Which type of music, popular in the 1950s, featured washboard, tea chest bass and other improvised instruments? **Skiffle**

7. What do you need to sup with the devil? **A long spoon**

8. Who warned Julius Caesar to beware the Ides of March in Shakespeare's play? **A soothsayer**

9. What was snooker referee Len Ganley advertising when he crushed a snooker ball to powder? **Carling Black Label**

10. According to an old rhyme, what does a sneeze on Wednesday signify? **A letter**

11. Who rush in where angels fear to tread? **Fools**

12. Who was Rudolph Raspe's baron who told such tall stories? **Munchausen**

13. Which English king was murdered at Berkeley Castle, traditionally by the insertion of a red hot iron into his body so that no external marks would be visible? **Edward II**

14. Which group had Top Ten hits with *Dancing Party*, *I Wonder Why* and *A Little Bit of Soap*? **Showaddywaddy**

15. Who played Test cricket for England in 1930 when he was 52 years old? **Wilfred Rhodes**

16. True or false: the *Flying Hamburger* was a diesel train? **True**

17. Which element has the Atomic Number 1? **Hydrogen**

18. Who had hits with *Homeward Bound*, *I Am a Rock* and *The Boxer*? **Simon and Garfunkel**

19. What is the name for a right-hander's off break delivered with a leg break action? **Googly**

20. In the British Telecom adverts on TV, what was Beattie's surname? **Bellman**

Quiz 101

1. What is jingoism? **Excessive patriotism**

2. Which water gate lies under St Thomas's Tower in the Tower of London? **Traitor's Gate**

3. In a famous story, who was Passepartout's master? **Phileas Fogg**

4. Which empire builder's last words were: "So little done; so much to do."? **Cecil Rhodes's**

5. Who won Best Actress Oscars for *Dangerous* and *Jezebel*? **Bette Davis**

6. Who played The Charmer in the TV series of the same name? **Nigel Havers**

7. Which gangleader's men were murdered in the St Valentine's Day Massacre? Was it Bugs Moran's, Legs Diamond's or Dutch Schultz's? **Bugs Moran's**

8. Which one word fits all these definitions: rubbish, drugs and a boat? **Junk**

9. What does a haematologist study? **The blood**

10. Which criminal was made into a romantic figure by the novel *Rookwood*? **Dick Turpin**

11. Which snake appears on the crown of Egyptian Pharaohs? **Cobra**

12. True or false: Jainism is an ancient religion. **True**

13. What is the capital of Bolivia? **La Paz**

14. Which star of the *Folies-Bergère* adopted a 'rainbow' family of children of different nationalities? **Josephine Baker**

15. Who painted *Derby Day* and *The Railway Station*? Was it Constable, Frith or Rossetti? **Frith**

16. What is the mother of invention? **Necessity**

17. In which TV series did Donna Reed step into Barbara Bel Geddes' shoes? ***Dallas***

18. Who won the Women's Olympic 100 metres in 1992? **Gail Devers**

19. In the UK, excluding mainland Britain, what is the largest island? Is it the Isle of Wight, Lewis with Harris or Skye? **Lewis with Harris**

20. Who had Top Ten hits in the 1980s with *Something About You*, *Lessons in Love* and *Running in the Family*? **Level 42**

Quiz 102

1. Which bubble burst in 1720 and caused a financial panic? **The South Sea Bubble**

2. Which US poetess married Ted Hughes and committed suicide aged 31? **Sylvia Plath**

3. Near which North American city are the Plains of Abraham? **Quebec**

4. Which great film star's last film was *Cuban Rebel Girls* in 1959? **Errol Flynn's**

5. Which Bishop signs himself Roffen? **Bishop of Rochester**

6. What did Perseus's helmet do for him? **Made him invisible**

7. The original Charing Cross was erected to commemorate Edward I's queen. What was her name? **Eleanor**

8. True or false: Dr Maria Montessori was an advocate of family planning? **False (She was an educationalist.)**

9. Elvis Presley had three successive No 1 hits in the UK charts in 1961. Name one. ***Are You Lonesome Tonight*, *Wooden Heart* or *Surrender***

10. Who played Mrs Robinson in the film *The Graduate*? **Anne Bancroft**

11. Near which Bavarian city did the Nazis hold huge rallies in the 1930s? **Nuremberg**

12. What form did the Egyptian god Sebek take? Was it a jackal, crocodile or hippopotamus? **Crocodile**

13. How many Olympics have been cancelled due to war? **Three**

14. Who wrote the novels *Rabbit, Run*, *Rabbit Redux* and *Rabbit Is Rich*? **John Updike**

15. In ballet, what does plié mean? Is it bending the body, bending the legs or bending the arms? **Bending the legs**

16. In the 1980s, who was the only non-American or European to win the Ladies' Singles at Wimbledon? **Evonne Cawley**

17. Who was Penny's boyfriend in *Just Good Friends*? **Vince**

18. Whom did the British, under Allenby, defeat at the Battle of Megiddo in World War 1? **The Turks**

19. What name is given to a small lake located in an abandoned meander loop of a river? **Oxbow lake**

20. What is the administrative HQ of Hampshire? **Winchester**

Quiz 103

1. What do you have if you possess encraty? **Self-control**

2. What is the term which means using a gentler expression to soften a harsh one? **Euphemism**

3. Which one word means very thin sheet metal, to baffle or thwart and a blunt sword? **Foil**

4. True or false: the Red Laws were a civil code of ancient Athens? **False (They were the Civil Code of Ancient Rome.)**

5. What is baccarat? **A card game**

6. Who created the naval character Hornblower? **C S Forester**

7. Which of the big cats have tear stain facial markings? **Cheetahs**

8. Who had Top Ten hits in the 1960s with *Together*, *Somewhere* and *Hold Me*? **P J Proby**

9. Who was the father of Henry I? Was it William I, Stephen or John? **William I**

10. In which TV series did Googie Withers play prison governor Faye Boswell? ***Within These Walls***

11. Steve Hislop won which trophy several times on a Honda? **Isle of Man TT Trophy**

12. With which children's TV programme would you associate Zippy, George and Bungle? ***Rainbow***

13. Which famous military group has its HQ at Aubagne near Marseilles? **Foreign Legion**

14. Which actress was stabbed in the shower in *Psycho*? **Janet Leigh**

15. The T-34, M-4 and Pz III were all what? **Tanks**

16. Which New Zealand writer created Roderick Alleyn of Scotland Yard? **Ngaio Marsh**

17. What was the trade name of the construction kits, introduced in 1907, consisting of metal strips with holes, screws, nuts, bolts, etc? **Meccano**

18. What is the magical kingdom in *The Lion, the Witch and the Wardrobe*? **Narnia**

19. Which US President's Presidency was called the Thousand Days? **J F Kennedy's**

20. True or false: Jimmy Nail reached No 1 with *Love Don't Live Here Anymore*? **False (No 3)**

Quiz 104

1. What is a fedora? **A hat**

2. Where is the Prado Art gallery? **Madrid**

3. Who anointed Saul and David as Kings of Israel? Was it Eli, Samuel or Daniel? **Samuel**

4. In which English county would you find the Devil's Bellows? **Cornwall**

5. What was the Christian name of suffragette Mrs Pankhurst? **Emmeline**

6. In Greek mythology, who was the messenger of the gods? **Hermes**

7. What is tansy? Is it a bird, a herb or a disease? **Herb**

8. Elmo Lincoln, Gene Polar, Jock Mahoney and Mike Henry have all played which screen hero? **Tarzan**

9. How many players are there on each side in Australian Rules Football? Is it 14, 16 or 18? **18**

10. Who played the title character in the TV series *My Wife Next Door*? **Hannah Gordon**

11. What are tested in the Trial of the Pyx ceremony? **Coins of the realm**

12. In tennis, who won gold in the Women's Singles in the 1996 Olympics? **Lindsay Davenport**

13. In the Bible, who wrote most of the Epistles? **St Paul**

14. In cricket, who scored England's first Test century? **W G Grace (1880)**

15. What does QU stand for in QUANGO? **Quasi**

16. True or false: Greta Garbo's last film was *Two-Faced Woman*? **True**

17. What is kohlrabi? **Vegetable (cabbage)**

18. Who or what would make use of musits or musets? **A hare (They are the gaps in a hedge through which a hunted hare escapes.)**

19. What sort of animal is a Lippizaner? **A horse**

20. Who played the title role in the film *The Millionairess*? **Sophia Loren**

Quiz 105

1. How many years are there in a millennium? **1000**

2. Which great bird carried off Sinbad the Sailor? **Roc or Rukh**

3. Which was the first country to win the Football World Cup in its own country? **Uruguay**

4. Who starred in the films *The Execution of Private Slovik*, *Badlands* and *Out of the Darkness*? **Martin Sheen**

5. Which American wrote *Astoria*, *The Legend of Sleepy Hollow* and *Bracebridge Hall*? **Washington Irving**

6. Was Charlie Chaplin's middle name Winston, Spencer or Burroughs? **Spencer**

7. Which country has the International Vehicle Registration Letter C? **Cuba**

8. Who had Top Ten hits with *Red Light Spells Danger*, *Suddenly* and *Caribbean Queen*? **Billy Ocean**

9. In the 19th century, what were Piccadilly Weepers? Were they knee ribbons, false eyelashes or droopy whiskers? **Droopy whiskers**

10. In *The Pardoner's Tale*, for what did the three rioters go looking? **Death**

11. Which sport is enjoyed by the Leander Club? **Rowing**

12. Who played Raffles in the TV series of the same name in the 1970s? **Anthony Valentine**

13. Which animals collect in a crash? **Rhinoceroses**

14. In which city is Schiphol airport? **Amsterdam**

15. What is the official language of Dominica? **English**

16. True or false: Cambrai was a battle in World War I? **True**

17. What was a ducat? **A coin**

18. In which city is the famous marble bridge called the Rialto? **Venice**

19. You would find information on what in *Debrett's*? **The Peerage**

20. Who played the male lead in *Blood Alley*, *The High and the Mighty* and *In Harm's Way*? **John Wayne**

Quiz 106

1. Which song begins: "Alas my love, you do me wrong to cast me off discourteously"? ***Greensleeves***

2. Who was court painter to Charles I? Was it Holbein, Van Dyck or Gainsborough? **Van Dyck**

3. Who connects *The Student Prince*, the TV series *Sword of Freedom* and *The Egyptian*? **Edmund Purdom**

4. Whom did Harold II succeed to the English throne? **Edward the Confessor**

5. Which famous novel has the characters Mulberry Hawk, Madeline Bray and Newman Noggs? ***Nicholas Nickleby***

6. With which sport are Bob Falkenberg, Dick Savitt and Ted Schroeder associated? **Tennis**

7. Who played Charlie Endell in *Budgie*? **Iain Cuthbertson**

8. What does the Glorious First of June commemorate? **A sea battle**

9. Who had Top Ten hits with *Got To Give It Up* and *Abraham Martin and John*? **Marvin Gaye**

10. In which country do 100 kobo equal 1 naira? Is it Nigeria, Ghana or Sierra Leone? **Nigeria**

11. With what was the Triangular Trade chiefly concerned? **Slaves**

12. True or false: the Zeppelin airship was never in commercial service? **False (1910 to 1914)**

13. Which black basalt slab, found by Napoleon's soldiers in Egypt, was the key to the translation of Egyptian hieroglyphic writing? **The Rosetta Stone**

14. Which king led the Huns from 445 to 450 AD? **Attila**

15. What was the name for the wooden head of a woman with a clay pipe in her mouth at fairs and at which people threw wooden balls? **Aunt Sally**

16. What is a taipan? An alligator, a snake or a boat? **A snake**

17. Are the Padang Highlands on Sumatra, Java or Borneo? **Sumatra**

18. Which Irish ghost is said to wail outside houses where a death is imminent? **Banshee**

19. Which one word means dry wine, to discharge and a hemp bag? **Sack**

20. Which actor was torn between Sigourney Weaver and Melanie Griffiths in *Working Girl*? **Harrison Ford**

Quiz 107

1. What, in the building trade, is called 'harling' in Scotland? **Pebble dash or rough cast**

2. Who had Top Twenty hits with *Legs* and *Gimme All Your Lovin'* and a No 22 with *Sharp-Dressed Man*? **ZZ Top**

3. Which Archbishop of Canterbury, who had supported Henry VIII's claim to be head of the Church of England, was burnt at the stake in 1556? **Thomas Cranmer**

4. In economics, according to Gresham's Law, what does bad money do? **Drives out good**

5. What would a Red Indian do with a parfleche? Would he carry articles in it, spread it on the floor of his tepee or wear it in his hair? **Carry articles (It is a bag.)**

6. Adam Bell, Clym of the Clough and William of Cloudesley were all famous what? **Archers**

7. Where in London would you see the White Tower? **Tower of London**

8. True or false: the town of Blarney is in County Donegal? **False (It is in Cork.)**

9. Which footballer became the then record signing for a transfer deal between two English football clubs on January 10th, 1995? **Andy Cole**

10. What began as the Christian Mission in Whitechapel in 1865? **Salvation Army**

11. What sort of guides were published by George Bradshaw? **Railway**

12. In which country was Andrew Carnegie born: was it Scotland, New Zealand or USA? **Scotland**

13. How many archangels are named in the Book of Enoch: 7, 13 or 99? **7**

14. Which hero married Bedr-el-Budur? Was it Aladdin, Ali Baba or Alexander the Great? **Aladdin**

15. Whose Top Ten hits included *What Is Love?*, *New Song* and *Pearl in the Shell*? **Howard Jones'**

16. What is your pollex? **Your thumb**

17. Which crimefighter was played by Peter Weller in a 1987 film? **Robocop**

18. Which novel features Colonel Creighton, Hurree Babu and Mahbub Ali? ***Kim***

19. In Norse mythology, what was Bifrost? Was it a giant tree, an eight-legged horse or a rainbow bridge? **A rainbow bridge**

20. What was the name of the character played by Ann Mitchell in *Widows* and *She's Out*? **Dolly Rawlins**

Quiz 108

1. In which hills is Cheddar Gorge? **Mendips**

2. Who, in the Bible, was the youngest son of Jacob? **Benjamin**

3. In cricket, what do the Australians call extras? **Sundries**

4. True or false: Sir Walter Scott wrote a novel called *The Black Dwarf*? **True**

5. Who made a Biblical riddle out of bees nesting in a dead lion? **Samson**

6. What was unusual about the Roman consul Incitatus? **He was a horse**

7. What does a cricket umpire signal by raising one arm horizontally? **No Ball**

8. Who made an album called *Highway 61 Revisited*? **Bob Dylan**

9. Which animal is Canada's official emblem? **Beaver**

10. For every seven white keys on a piano, how many black keys are there? **Five**

11. What is the green-eyed monster? **Jealousy**

12. In ancient days, what was a carrack? Was it a barrel, a ship or a weapon? **A ship**

13. In which game are flattened iron rings thrown at a hob? **Quoits**

14. Which country's official name is Daehan (or Taehan) Minkuk (or Minguk)? **South Korea's**

15. Who played Danny Kaye's leading lady in three films, James Cagney's wife in *White Heat* and Burt Lancaster's love interest in *The Flame and the Arrow*? **Virginia Mayo**

16. Which tough guy actor's last film was *The Carpetbaggers*? **Alan Ladd's**

17. With which instrument is Max Roach associated? **Drums**

18. Who had Top Ten hits with *Don't Answer Me*, *Conversations* and *It's For You*? **Cilla Black**

19. In which school did Fives originate? **Eton**

20. Ryeland, Kerry Hill and Roscommon are all breeds of which animal? **Sheep**

Quiz 109

1. What word was used for the eastern end of the Mediterranean and the adjoining countries? **Levant**

2. Who chaired *Have I Got News For You?* and acted in *One Foot In the Grave*? **Angus Deayton**

3. In Genesis, which land was said to lie to the east of Eden? **Nod**

4. Maximilian was installed as emperor of which country by Napoleon III? **Mexico**

5. What is a phalarope? Is it a bird, a microbe or a formation of troops? **Bird**

6. True or false: the first US Open Golf championship was played on a 9 hole course? **True**

7. Which football club did Gary Lineker leave to join Tottenham Hotspur? **Barcelona**

8. By what name was Mohammed Ahmed, the man who took Khartoum in 1885, known? **The Mahdi**

9. What name is given to a person or thing that brings bad luck? **Jinx or Jonah**

10. What does a gamophobe fear? **Marriage**

11. A slave, Toussaint L'Overture, led a revolt of blàck slaves which overthrew the government of which country in 1791? **Haiti**

12. In mythology, what happened if you drank the water of the River Lethe? **You forgot**

13. Who played Blott in the TV serial *Blott on the Landscape*? **David Suchet**

14. Under what guise does Caroline Hook appear on television? **Mrs Merton**

15. What binding medium is used in gouache painting? Is it egg white, egg yolk or glue? **Glue**

16. Exactly where is your coccyx? **Base of spine**

17. Which character has been played in films by, among others, Frank Langella, Jack Palance, Gary Oldman and Francis Lederer? **Dracula**

18. Who had a No 1 hit in 1982 with *Happy Talk*? **Captain Sensible**

19. What are Ashvine Challenger, Old Hooky, White Boar and Hard Tackle? **Real ales**

20. Which metal is extracted from Sphalerite? **Zinc**

Quiz 110

1. Which food was miraculously supplied to the Israelites in the wilderness? **Manna**

2. True or false: prosthetics is the science of creating and fitting artificial limbs? **True**

3. Who had a 1986 No 1 with *The Lady in Red*? **Chris de Burgh**

4. Complete this nautical trio: the *Pinta*, the *Nina* and the . . . (what)? ***Santa Maria***

5. What is the opposite of 'dunce'? **Dux**

6. Who succeeded Anthony Eden as Prime Minister? **Harold Macmillan**

7. A leopard's head, an anchor, a castle and a harp are all used as what? **Hallmarks**

8. Who is the first female in the order of accession to the British throne? **Princess Beatrice**

9. In the Bible, who was sent into the Land of Nod as a punishment? **Cain**

10. Which English King accepted the reform plan known as The Provisions of Oxford? **Henry III**

11. Which one word means to cultivate, up to the time of and a money drawer? **Till**

12. Who was the first team to win the FA Cup at Wembley? **Bolton Wanderers**

13. Who led the bank robbers in the film *The League of Gentlemen*? **Jack Hawkins**

14. Which poem begins famously with the lines "I leant upon a coppice gate / When Frost was spectre-gray"? ***The Darkling Thrush***

15. Which Gilbert and Sullivan operetta has the subtitle *The King of Barataria*? ***The Gondoliers***

16. Who said, after winning the Grand National: "Sex is an anti-climax after that"? **Mick Fitzgerald**

17. What is the capital of New York state? **Albany**

18. True or false: SOS is not an abbreviation for Save Our Souls? **True**

19. What name is given to the stiffening of the body after death? **Rigor mortis**

20. When does puerperal fever strike? **After childbirth**

Quiz 111

1. In what year did Queen Victoria die? **1901**

2. Who played Isadora Duncan in the film *Isadora*? **Vanessa Redgrave**

3. In which Italian city can you see Juliet's house and balcony? Is it Genoa, Bologna or Verona? **Verona**

4. Whose life is dealt with in the novel *The Big Fisherman*? **Simon (St) Peter's**

5. By what name was writer Mary Westmacott better known? **Agatha Christie**

6. Which song contains these lines: "People come to their windows. They all stare at me. Shake their heads in sorrow, saying 'Who can that fool be?' "? ***Walking in the Rain***

7. What nationality was World Motor Racing Champion Juan Fangio? **Argentinian**

8. Apart from a dance, what is a bolero? **Short jacket**

9. Which artist's biography was entitled *The Fake's Progress*? **Tom Keating's**

10. Who created Noggin the Nog, Bagpuss and The Clangers? **Oliver Postgate**

11. In which African country was the TV series *The Flame Trees of Thika* set? **Kenya**

12. Who had Top Ten hits with *Body Talk*, *Just an Illusion* and *Music and Lights*? **Imagination**

13. Which fluid remains after the blood has clotted? **Serum**

14. True or false: the Bible says Delilah cut off Samson's hair? **False (She had a man do it.)**

15. Who, in 1992, broke Pat Eddery's run of four consecutive Flat Jockey Championships? **Michael Roberts**

16. Who designed the fighter bomber the Mosquito? **De Havilland**

17. Who played Officer Barraclough in *Porridge*? **Brian Wilde**

18. In a well-known song, who was thrown out "with nothing but a fine tooth comb"? **Bill Bailey**

19. What is a half hunter? **A pocket watch**

20. What are the grades of proficiency in judo called? **Dans**

Quiz 112

1. If you were described as an ectomorph, would you be fat, thin, tall, short or pale? **Thin**

2. On what is pomade used? **The hair/skin of the head**

3. What is champaign? **Flat, open country**

4. Is a brumby a wild horse, a thorny bush or a standing stone? **A wild horse**

5. What is the chemical symbol for arsenic? **As**

6. Which Canadian province is named after one of Queen Victoria's daughters? **Alberta**

7. What was the first country to use number plates on its road vehicles? Was it Britain, the USA or France? **France**

8. Whose Top Ten hits included *Let Me In*, *The Proud One* and *Going Home*? **The Osmonds'**

9. True or false: Gustav Holst called Neptune *The Bringer of War*? **False (*The Mystic*)**

10. Which Welsh bay lies between St Govan's Head and Worms Head? **Camarthen Bay**

11. To what does the old saying 'Dog goes, cat comes' refer? **The waxing and waning of the moon**

12. Who got to No 3 with *Joe le Taxi*? **Vanessa Paradis**

13. What is the Scottish word for a rough cottage or hut where farm workers lived? **Bothy**

14. In the British Telecom adverts, which actor said "It's good to talk"? **Bob Hoskins**

15. What would you be doing if you practised banting: yachting, dieting or crochet? **Dieting**

16. Which of D H Lawrence's novels is set in Australia? ***Kangaroo***

17. What was the Derby Scheme of 1915? Was it conscription, dole or food vouchers? **Conscription**

18. Who played the lead in the films *The Joker is Wild*, *A Hole in the Head* and *Never So Few*? **Frank Sinatra**

19. Which country was formerly called Dutch East Indies? **Indonesia**

20. Which one word means fill with water and sink, an originator and a person who casts metal? **Founder**

Quiz 113

1. In *Rising Damp*, which character was the son of an African tribal chief? **Philip**

2. Which Berkshire school did Prince Charles attend? **Cheam**

3. Timbrology was an old name for bell-ringing, tree felling or stamp collecting? Which? **Stamp collecting**

4. What did Mark Twain describe as "a cabbage with a college education"? **Cauliflower**

5. True or false: Pearl Buck was the first woman to win the Nobel prize for Literature? **False**

6. Who was known as the Widow at Windsor? **Queen Victoria**

7. What was Winston Churchill's home in Kent called? **Chartwell**

8. What was the ancient name of Iraq? **Mesopotamia**

9. Of which modern instrument was the sackbut a forerunner? **Trombone**

10. In the drink 'Gin and It' what is 'It'? **Italian Vermouth**

11. Who played the headmaster in the TV series *Whack-O*? **Jimmy Edwards**

12. Whose musical works were catalogued by Kochel numbers? **Mozart's**

13. Who played the female lead to Rock Hudson in *Magnificent Obsession*? **Jane Wyman**

14. In the Bible, who was the father of Enoch? **Cain**

15. What does 'sub rosa' mean? **In secret**

16. Which was the only No 1 for the Dave Clark Five? ***Glad All Over***

17. Which fish is known as Fish Royal? **Sturgeon**

18. Manganese Bronze Holdings are the makers of which famous vehicle? **Black taxis**

19. *Dwt* was an abbreviation for what? **Pennyweight**

20. Which sport was played by Peanut Louie? **Lawn Tennis**

Quiz 114

1. Which country was ruled by the Empress Elizabeth until 1762? **Russia**
2. Which famous lawman had the middle names Berry Stapp? **Wyatt Earp**
3. Which Italian monastery was destroyed in the Allied advance on Rome when it was a key point in the German defence line? **Monte Cassino**
4. The philosopher Epicurus said: "[it] has never done a man good and he is lucky if it has not harmed him." What was he talking about? **Sexual intercourse**
5. Which TV celebrity received an Oscar nomination for her part in the film *The Color Purple*? **Oprah Winfrey**
6. Who was chief engineer of the Great Western Railway from 1833? **Isambard Kingdom Brunel**
7. If a ewe is a sheep, what is a ewer? **A water jug**
8. Who wrote *The History of the Decline and Fall of the Roman Empire*? **Gibbon**
9. Where would you find the Queen's Robing Room, St Stephen's Hall and the Victoria Tower? **Houses of Parliament**
10. Who composed *Danse Macabre* and *The Carnival of the Animals*? **Saint-Saens**
11. True or false: César Auguste Franck was a famous scientist? **False (Composer)**
12. Is hafnium a Jewish ceremony, an element or an Oriental dagger? **An element**

13. What is the capital of Wyoming? **Cheyenne**

14. Who became British Prime Minister in 1916? **Lloyd George**

15. Name one of the two books in the Old Testament named after women? **Ruth or Esther**

16. Which Chinese city gave its name to the forcing of men to become sailors against their will? **Shanghai**

17. Which ancient city state had magistrates called Ephori? **Sparta**

18. Clapper, truss and bascule are all types of what? **Bridge**

19. In which field did Georg Wilhelm Pabst achieve fame? **Cinema (Director)**

20. Which Roman poet wrote *Ars Amatoria* and *Metamorphoses*? **Ovid**

Quiz 115

1. Which creatures congregate in a muster? **Peacocks**

2. Which English county has borders with Cheshire, Hereford & Worcester, Staffordshire and Wales? **Shropshire**

3. What is the capital of Zimbabwe? **Harare**

4. Which poem by George Crabbe was made into an opera by Benjamin Britten? ***Peter Grimes***

5. Which novelist's middle names were John Huffham? **Charles Dickens'**

6. Where would you find a ledger line? **On a musical score**

7. Which annual publication was first published in 1700 under the title *Voices of the Stars*? ***Old Moore's Almanac***

8. Who directed the films *Mean Streets*, *Taxi Driver* and *Raging Bull*? **Martin Scorsese**

9. Who rode Slip Anchor to win the 1985 Derby? **Steve Cauthen**

10. Which animals are attacked by the disease rinderpest? **Cattle**

11. Who wrote the boys' adventure stories *Coral Island* and *Martin Rattler*? **R M Ballantyne**

12. Who was the first man to hold both land and water speed records simultaneously? **Malcolm Campbell**

13. Which French-Canadian became Prime Minister of Canada in 1968? **Pierre Trudeau**

14. What is the most southerly point of the American continent? **Cape Horn**

15. In which bay is the island of Capri? **Bay of Naples**

16. Apart from *Go Now* and *Question* what was the Moody Blues' only other Top Ten hit? ***Nights in White Satin***

17. Which Italian boxer won the World Heavyweight title when he knocked out Jack Sharkey in 1933? **Primo Carnera**

18. Which *Alice* character said: "You might just as well say that 'I see what I eat' is the same as 'I eat what I see'."? **(Mad) Hatter**

19. What nationality was the dancer Isadora Duncan? **American**

20. What sort of fruit are white hearts, black hearts, dukes and amarelles? **Cherries**

Quiz 116

1. From 1739 until 1979, which country's symbol of monarchy was the Peacock Throne? **(Persia) Iran**

2. Leaving San Francisco via the Golden Gate bridge, in which direction are you travelling? **North**

3. Which English king spent only five months of his ten year reign in England? **Richard I**

4. What do Mexicans call the Rio Grande? **Rio Bravo**

5. For her part in which film did Margaret Rutherford receive an Oscar? ***The VIPs***

6. To a nautical man, what is a gollywobbler? **A sail**

7. What was the name of Derek Fowlds' character in TV's *Heartbeat*? **Sgt (Oscar) Blaketon**

8. Most of Lake Rudolf is in which African country? **Kenya**

9. Who was the last Pope whose name was not John, Paul or Pius? **Benedict XV**

10. Which country has a capital whose name means Bay of Smoke because of the steam from nearby geysers? **Iceland**

11. Which star's only chart hit was *The Man That Got Away* in 1955? **Judy Garland**

12. Kings from four countries are said to be buried on Iona. There are Scottish, French and Irish kings and kings from which other country? **Norway**

13. What is the official name of Hull? **Kingston-upon-Hull**

14. In which Russian city was the Winter Palace, stormed in 1917? **St Petersburg (Leningrad or Petrograd are acceptable.)**

15. Which team did Dennis Mortimer captain to the Football League Title in 1981? **Aston Villa**

16. By what name is the Roman poet Quintus Horatius Flaccus more commonly known? **Horace**

17. Which English astronomer wrote *The Nature of the Universe* and *Frontiers of Astronomy*? **Fred Hoyle**

18. What was Charles Perrault's most famous collection of fairy stories called? ***Tales of Mother Goose***

19. Which TV series was set in Kirby Newtown? ***Z Cars***

20. Which trading company was granted a royal charter for trade in Canada in 1670? **Hudson's Bay Company**

Quiz 117

1. True or false: a Turk's Head is a type of knot? **True**

2. How old is a quadragenarian? **40**

3. Proverbially, when is the darkest hour? **Before the dawn**

4. In which county is the resort of Budleigh Salterton? **Devon**

5. In our language from 1957, what's the Russian for 'travelling companion'? **Sputnik**

6. Which bird was once known as the halcyon? **Kingfisher**

7. What was hokey-pokey, sold on the streets until the 1920s? Was it icc-cream, toffee or dried fish? **Ice cream**

8. Who starred in *Death in Venice*, *The Damned* and *The Servant*? **Dirk Bogarde**

9. Which TV presenter said: "There was life before *Coronation Street*, but it didn't add up to much."? **Russell Harty**

10. Which puppet on TV was operated by Ivan Owen? **Basil Brush**

11. What would you do with spelding: solder, weave cloth or eat it? **Eat it (Fish)**

12. The book *Enemy Coast Ahead* was made into which famous film? ***The Dambusters***

13. Which of these is a diamond: Star of Bethlehem, Star of India or Star of South Africa? **Star of South Africa**

14. Who sang with Elton John on *Act of War*? **Millie Jackson**

15. Which flower is the badge of the Boy Scouts? **Fleur de Lis**

16. How far south did Bonnie Prince Charlie get in 1745? **To Derby**

17. True or false: the poet A E Housman is associated with Cornwall? **False (Shropshire)**

18. Whose early films included *The Song of Bernadette* and *Laura* before he made *House of Wax*? **Vincent Price**

19. On which river does Leicester stand? **River Soar**

20. Who, in 1967, became Britain's first Minister for the Arts? **Jennie Lee**

Quiz 118

1. Which song begins: "When you left me all alone, at the record hop; told me you were going out for a soda pop"? ***Lipstick On Your Collar***

2. How long would you have been married if you were celebrating a Platinum Anniversary? **70 years**

3. Where are the Highland Games held? **Braemar**

4. What happened near Cheddington in Buckinghamshire on 7th August, 1963? **Great Train Robbery**

5. Which country was ruled by King Gustavus Adolphus, the Lion of the North, in the 17th century? **Sweden**

6. Who wrote *The Aspern Papers*, *The Ambassadors* and *The Golden Bowl*? **Henry James**

7. Who wrote the plays *The Glass Menagerie* and *Cat On a Hot Tin Roof*? **Tennessee Williams**

8. Who played the rich rock star in the TV series *Roll Over, Beethoven*? **Nigel Planer**

9. Who succeeded Bob Paisley as manager of Liverpool Football Club? **Joe Fagan**

10. Who defected to Russia with Guy Burgess in 1951? **Donald MacLean**

11. Of which soldier did Tennyson write: "This earth has borne no simpler, nobler, man."? Was it Wellington, Marlborough or Gordon? **Gordon**

12. Who had Top Twenty hits with *I Feel Free*, *Strange Brew* and *Badge*? **Cream**

13. The mastiff and the greyhound were crossed to produce which breed of dog? **Great Dane**

14. Who directed the film *Bird*, the film biography of Charlie Parker? **Clint Eastwood**

15. What is the capital of the Orkneys? **Kirkwall**

16. What is a monopole? **A radio aerial**

17. What was the middle name of the writer William Thackeray? **Makepeace**

18. Where do bees carry the pollen they collect? **On their back legs (in a 'basket')**

19. Osbert, Sacheverell and Edith . . . What is the surname? **Sitwell**

20. For what did Madame Helen Blavatsky achieve fame? **Spiritualism**

Quiz 119

1. On TV, who played *The Man From Atlantis*? **Patrick Duffy**

2. What pseudonym was used by Aurore Dupin, mistress of Chopin? **George Sand**

3. To what did the Spastics Society change its name in the 1990s? Was it Assist, Care or Scope? **Scope**

4. For what product is the island of Murano, off Venice, famous? **Glass**

5. There were five Roman Emperors in 68-69 AD. Galba, Otho and Vitellius were three of them; name one of the other two. **Nero or Vespasian**

6. Which word means the knack of making lucky discoveries by accident? **Serendipity**

7. Which part of your body would suffer from trichosis? **The hair**

8. Who played Major Harry Truscott in the TV series *Fairly Secret Army*? **Geoffrey Palmer**

9. Who wrote the novels *Pied Piper*, *No Highway* and *A Town Like Alice*? **Nevil Shute**

10. Who had Top Ten hits with *Woman in Love*, *My Simple Heart* and *Take Good Care of Yourself*? **The Three Degrees**

11. Which political party's HQ is at 150 Walworth Road in London? **Labour Party's**

12. True or false: Prince Charles is the Earl of Inverness? **False (It is Prince Andrew.)**

13. What name is given to Buddhist shrines built in the form of a tower? **Pagodas**

14. What is the popular name for the antirrhinum? **Snapdragon**

15. Which word, used in proofreading, means 'Leave as printed' or 'Let it stand'? **Stet**

16. Who played a female undertaker in the TV series *In Loving Memory*? **Thora Hird**

17. In the Tarzan novels, who was known as Korak? **Tarzan's son**

18. Why should flags be flown on Government buildings on February 6th? **Anniversary of the Queen's accession**

19. Who headed the committee investigating 'sleaze' in public life in 1995? **Lord Nolan**

20. What is a titi? Is it a small crocodile, a tropical songbird or a monkey? **A monkey**

Quiz 120

1. Who played the title role in the comedy film *The Missionary*? **Michael Palin**

2. Who was the mother-in-law of Angus Ogilvy? **Princess Marina**

3. Who wrote *Puck of Pook's Hill* and *Rewards and Fairies*? **Rudyard Kipling**

4. What sort of weapon was an arbalest? Was it a musket, a mace or a crossbow? **A crossbow**

5. Which frigate was launched secretly in 1986 in Wallsend to replace a ship lost in the Falklands? **HMS *Coventry***

6. Who had Top Ten hits with *Best Years of Our Lives*, *High Life* and *Ay Ay Ay Ay Moosey*? **Modern Romance**

7. Of whom did Dennis Healey say that being attacked by him was like being savaged by a dead sheep? **Geoffrey Howe**

8. True or false: the Thames is the longest river wholly in England? **True**

9. What is the capital of Manitoba province in Canada? **Winnipeg**

10. In which county is the Parliamentary constituency of South Hams? **Devon**

11. Who was banned for two one-day cricket internationals in 1986 after admitting he had smoked cannabis? **Ian Botham**

12. Which domestic pet is descended from the cavy? **Guinea-pig**

13. Who wrote *A Farewell To Arms* and *Death in the Afternoon*? **Ernest Hemingway**

14. Which TV series featured the character Boss Hogg? ***The Dukes of Hazzard***

15. In the nursery rhyme *Cock A Doodle Doo*, what has my master lost? **His fiddling stick**

16. What name is given to ornamental gilded bronze, used to decorate furniture? **Ormolu**

17. What was the name of Don Lang's backing group? **The Frantic Five**

18. As what did Walt Whitman make his name? **A poet**

19. What was the title of the modern film version of *Cyrano de Bergerac* starring Steve Martin as a fire chief? ***Roxanne***

20. In which country was the military Tet Offensive launched in 1968? **South Vietnam**

Quiz 121

1. Which part of the body is affected by Crohn's Disease? **Intestines**

2. Is a jockteleg a bread roll, a clasp-knife or a ribbon tied round the stockings? **Clasp-knife**

3. In which US town is the Rose Bowl, venue for the post season football game between college champions? **Pasadena**

4. True or false: Harry Houdini was born in Budapest? **True**

5. Where was "the shot heard all around the world" fired? **Sarajevo**

6. What nationality was Canute, King of England from 1016 to 1035? **Danish**

7. What sort of garment was a Sloppy Joe? **A loose sweater**

8. Which famous radio programme ended with the words "Carry on, London"? ***In Town Tonight***

9. Which palace was given to the Duke of Marlborough as a reward for military services? **Blenheim**

10. J McGill, A Long and T Watson all won British championships in which of the following: marbles, draughts or quoits? **Draughts**

11. Who played Don Quixote in the film *Man of La Mancha*? **Peter O'Toole**

12. Whose Top Ten hits included *Oh Well*, *Man of the World* and *Tusk*? **Fleetwood Mac's**

13. Which musical TV series was described as "sheer filth, obnoxious and bordering on pornography" when first broadcast in 1978? ***Pennies From Heaven***

14. In what field was the Bauhaus movement? **Architecture**

15. What was the title of the famous folklore study by Sir J G Frazer? ***The Golden Bough***

16. The Whittaker system divides the living world into how many kingdoms? Is it 5, 7 or 12? **5**

17. What was silent film star Fatty Arbuckle's Christian name? **Roscoe**

18. What was the name of the spiv played by James Beck in *Dad's Army*? **Walker**

19. Desmond, Taiwan, Douglas and Pattie are all slang words for what? **Academic Degrees**

20. True or false: the German U-Boat U-65, launched in 1916, was said to be haunted? **True**

Quiz 122

1. Which rat trained the Teenage Mutant Ninja Turtles? **Splinter**

2. Which element is last alphabetically? **Zirconium**

3. *The Flowers o' the Forest* is a traditional lament for Scots who fell where? **Flodden**

4. Who said: "Don't point that beard at me: it might go off."? **Groucho Marx**

5. In the poem *Beowulf*, how does Beowulf die? **Killed by a dragon**

6. What is the administrative HQ of Shropshire? **Shrewsbury**

7. Ben Webster, Lester Young and Steve Lacy are all associated with which instrument? **Saxophone**

8. Who published the book *Missionary Travels in South Africa* in 1857? **David Livingstone**

9. Which British city contains the Jew's House, the Usher Gallery and the National Cycle Museum? **Lincoln**

10. Under what pseudonym did Sir William Connor write in *The Daily Mirror*? **Cassandra**

11. What was the subject of the Mel Brooks' film subtitled *Men in Tights*? **Robin Hood**

12. From where does Cathay Pacific Airways come? **Hong Kong**

13. Eric Idle and Neil Innes sent up the Beatles by forming which group on TV? **The Rutles**

14. Which Elvis film was based on the play *A Stone For Danny Fisher*? ***King Creole***

15. Which US union, formerly led by Jimmy Hoffa, was at one time the largest in the USA? **Teamsters**

16. True or false: the 'Pilot' in the famous Punch cartoon *Dropping the Pilot* refers to Bismarck? **True**

17. Which sport might involve a schuss? **Skiing**

18. In Greek mythology, what did the gods eat? **Ambrosia**

19. Who had Top Ten hits with *I Can't Explain*, *Happy Jack* and *Pictures of Lily*? **The Who**

20. What relation was William the Conqueror to King Stephen? **Grandfather**

Quiz 123

1. Which Brontë sister wrote *Shirley*? **Charlotte**

2. What does the expression "The old woman is plucking her goose" mean? **It's snowing**

3. Where are your zygomatic, ethmoid and vomer bones? **In the skull**

4. What was the setting for the 1987 film *Gardens of Stone*? **Arlington National Cemetery**

5. Which Football League club plays at Springfield Park? **Wigan Athletic**

6. What is a young kangaroo called? **A Joey**

7. Nobles, unites, bezants and angels were all what? **Coins**

8. Where on a ship would you find the lubber's hole? **On the mast**

9. What was the title of the 1966 TV series about a cockney charlady, played by Kathleen Harrison, who inherited an industrial empire? ***Mrs Thursday***

10. The character 'Old Mortality' devoted his life to doing what? Was it planting fruit trees, cleaning and restoring tombstones or burying paupers? **Cleaning and restoring tombstones**

11. What is a bissextile year? **A leap year**

12. True or false: there is a country called the Federated States of Micronesia? **True**

13. What must when the Devil drives? **Needs**

14. Which English king was nicknamed The Merry Monarch? **Charles II**

15. Before Frank Spencer, "Some mothers do 'ave 'em" was a catchphrase in whose comedy radio programme? **Jimmy Clitheroe's**

16. Who played the other half of *The Odd Couple* when Tony Randall played Felix? **Jack Klugman**

17. In Norse mythology, which maidens conduct fallen heroes to Valhalla? **The Valkyries**

18. To what did Pussyfoot Johnson devote his energy? Was it legalising brothels, temperance or a detective agency? **Temperance**

19. What is a Miller's Thumb? Is it a type of bean, a fish or a tallow candle? **Fish (Bullhead)**

20. Where did 'expects' replace 'confides' to save the number of flags? **Trafalgar (In Nelson's famous signal.)**

Quiz 124

1. Who had Top Ten hits with *The Cutter* and *The Killing Moon*? **Echo and the Bunnymen**
2. Who wrote the plays *The Cocktail Party* and *The Family Reunion*? **T S Eliot**
3. What was the name of Kaiser Bill's mother? **Victoria**
4. Who played Malcolm X in the 1992 film of that name? **Denzel Washington**
5. Olympia is the capital of which US state? **Washington**
6. Which Sheridan play features Sir Lucius O'Trigger and Anthony Absolute? ***The Rivals***
7. By what name is Agnes Gonxha Bejaxhui better known? Is she Mother Teresa, Michelle Pfeiffer or Bette Midler? **Mother Teresa**
8. True or false: the first Porsche was a sports version of the Volkswagen Beetle? **True**
9. In which city is Suffolk's administrative HQ? **Ipswich**
10. For what was Gerardus Mercator famous? **Maps of the earth**
11. Who had No 1 hits with *I Love You* and *The Minute You're Gone*? **Cliff Richard**

12. Which one word means a loud noise, an account of a speech and a statement of a pupil's work?
Report

13. In a 1995 survey, which capital was rated Europe's cleanest? Was it London, Athens or Paris?
London

14. Which of the Shetland Isles is regarded as Britain's most remote island? **Foula**

15. What was the name of George Stephenson's first locomotive? ***Blucher***

16. In which English county is the Wyre Forest?
Worcestershire

17. Which game birds' group name is a tok?
Capercaillie

18. Which of the following has the most fat content: bacon, almonds or Cheddar cheese? **Almonds**

19. Which Briton broke the world land speed record at Daytona in 1927 and 1929? **Henry Segrave**

20. Who played the monster in the film *Young Frankenstein*? **Peter Boyle**

Quiz 125

1. Which woodwind instrument is also called the octave flute? **Piccolo**

2. What nickname was given in World War 2 to scientists or backroom boys? **Boffins**

3. In which sport would you use the term 'flanconnade'? **Fencing**

4. True or false: John Dryden was the first official Poet Laureate? **True**

5. What is supernaculum? Is it fine wine, part of a building or part of a horse's harness? **Fine wine**

6. Which country lies between Algeria and Libya? **Tunisia**

7. Which TV show produced the catch phrases "Sock it to me", "Here come de Judge" and "Very interesting – but stupid"? ***Rowan and Martin's Laugh-In***

8. Which actress was Oscar nominated for *Silkwood* and won an Oscar for *Moonstruck*? **Cher**

9. Who are members of the Q Guild? **Butchers**

10. For what is Chinge Hall in Lancashire famous? **It is haunted**

11. Where was the first tennis club founded in England? Was it Leamington Spa, Wimbledon or Bath? **Leamington Spa**

12. William Adams, who learned to sail with Francis Drake, later became so respected in a foreign country that to this day they hold an annual festival in his honour. Which country? Is it Holland, Japan or Denmark? **Japan**

13. Which literary prize has been won by *Injury Time*, *Hawksmoor* and *Picture Palace*? **Whitbread Award**

14. Which British ship – a liner – was the first to be sunk by a U-Boat on the first day of World War 2? ***Athenia***

15. Who was the last European king to be assassinated? Was it Alexander I of Jugoslavia, Carlos I of Spain or Giorgios II of Greece? **Alexander I**

16. Whose Top Ten hits included *Johnny Come Home* and *Suspicious Minds*? **Fine Young Cannibals**

17. Where exactly in your body is fibrin found? **In the blood**

18. If someone carried out rolfing on you, would they be massaging you, telling your fortune or showing you card tricks? **Massaging**

19. In which country did the King of Alba rule? **Scotland**

20. Who plays Max Farnham in the TV soap *Brookside*? **Steve Pinder**

Quiz 126

1. Who wrote *The Fourth Protocol*? **Frederick Forsyth**

2. Which word means a dollar, a male rabbit and a back-arching jump? **Buck**

3. Whose Top Ten hits include *How Will I Know*, *Greatest Love of All* and *So Emotional*? **Whitney Houston's**

4. Which common gas was once called azote? **Nitrogen**

5. Whose catchphrase was "Mind my bike"? **Jack Warner's**

6. According to Shakespeare's play, who was Prince of Tyre? **Pericles**

7. What kind of song is a berceuse? **A lullaby or cradle-song**

8. What is the official language of the Ivory Coast? **French**

9. Which medal now ranks second to the Victoria Cross for bravery? **Conspicuous Gallantry Cross**

10. Which common bird is also called the dunnock? **Hedge Sparrow**

11. According to the nursery rhyme, what kind of cake were the fighting lion and unicorn given? **Plum cake**

12. Which film starts with Mel Brooks and Anne Bancroft singing *Sweet Georgia Brown* in Polish? ***To Be or Not To Be* (1983)**

13. What was a bridewell? **A prison**

14. Who bought the Castle of Mey in 1952? **The Queen Mother**

15. Who played a delayed headmaster in the film *Clockwise*? **John Cleese**

16. True or false: Alexander the Great died at Alexandria? **False (Babylon)**

17. Who played the title role in the film *Forrest Gump*? **Tom Hanks**

18. What is a gonk? **A furry toy**

19. What is the capital of the Dominican republic? **Santo Domingo**

20. Who played the forever changing scientist in *The Incredible Hulk*? **Bill Bixby**

Quiz 127

1. Which English city had the Latin name Pons Aelius? **Newcastle-upon-Tyne**

2. What, astronomically, ends at the vernal equinox? **Winter**

3. In which sport did John Tate, Greg Page and Tony Tubbs all become World Champions? **Boxing**

4. Which disease is caused by excess uric acid in the blood and inflammation of the joints? **Gout**

5. What is the main metal in the alloy known as gun metal? **Copper**

6. Which former capital of Japan is actually an anagram of the present capital? **Kyoto**

7. In which country is the 1000 mile long Mackenzie River? **Canada**

8. What was the nickname of Henry Percy, son of the 1st Earl of Northumberland? **Hotspur**

9. Which big star made his film debut in *Revenge of the Creature*, appeared in *Tarantula* and *Escapade in Japan* and in recent years has starred in *Pink Cadillac* and *The Rookie*? **Clint Eastwood**

10. Who succeeded Jawaharlal (Pandit) Nehru as Prime Minister of India? **Lal Shastri**

11. With which TV series do you associate characters called Recall, Sicknote, Bayleaf and Hallam? ***London's Burning***

12. What language is spoken by South Africans of Boer descent? **Afrikaans**

13. Which Derbyshire town has a church famous for its crooked spire? **Chesterfield**

14. The Curtana, the Rod with the Dove, the Spurs, the Armills and the Ampulla are all parts of what? **Crown Jewels**

15. In which African country do the Berber people, the Riffs, live? **Morocco**

16. Which of the Channel Islands has a parliament called the Chief Pleas but no income tax and no cars? **Sark**

17. What was the subject of the Wolfenden report of 1957? **Homosexuality and Prostitution**

18. What name is given to the low-lying tracts of land west and south of the Wash? **The Fens**

19. Who produced albums called *Armed Forces*, *Trust* and *Blood and Chocolate*? **Elvis Costello**

20. In which American state are the Blue Ridge Mountains, Arlington National Cemetery and Shenandoah National Park? **Virginia**

Quiz 128

1. At which battle in 1513 was James IV of Scotland killed? **Flodden**

2. How should the wife of a Knight be addressed? **Lady**

3. Which great entertainer was born in St Petersburg in 1885 and died in the USA in 1950? **Al Jolson**

4. For whom in the Old Testament did Jacob's son, Joseph, work as a steward? **Potiphar**

5. Corner bridle, oblique stub and half-lap are all terms used in . . . (what)? **Joinery/Carpentry**

6. Which country had a socialist political group in the 20th century called the Spartacus League? **Germany**

7. What is a teleost? Is it a fish, a Greek garment or an echo? **A fish**

8. What is the chemical symbol for potassium? **K**

9. What apparatus, which became a popular child's toy, was devised by David Brewster in 1816 for experiments in reflection? **Kaleidoscope**

10. Which part of the body is affected by keratitis? **The eye**

11. Which body of water is to the east of Kenya? **Indian Ocean**

12. Which capital city lies where the Blue and White Niles meet? **Khartoum**

13. Which tree is known by the names Anagris, Pea Tree, Golden Chain, Golden Rain and Beane Trefoyle? **Laburnum**

14. Which German family firm produced most of Germany's arms and armaments in both World Wars? **Krupp**

15. What made its first broadcast on New Year's Eve in 1923? **Big Ben**

16. Which Shakepearean character says to Charmian: "Come, let's to billiards."? **Cleopatra**

17. Which bird, according to legend, got its colours by flying towards the setting sun with night at its back when it left Noah's Ark? **Kingfisher**

18. Which organ forms and secretes bile? **Liver**

19. Whose 1942 Report laid the foundations of the welfare state? **William Beveridge's**

20. Which 1990 film about medical students experimenting with death took its title from what is seen on a monitor screen when somebody dies? ***Flatliners***

Quiz 129

1. Bismarck said: "The great questions of our day cannot be solved by speeches and majority votes but by . . . (what)"? **Blood and iron**

2. Which common edible object's name literally means "twice cooked"? **Biscuit**

3. Who composed the operettas *Gipsy Love*, *The Land of Smiles* and *The Merry Widow*? **Franz Lehar**

4. Which film star, nicknamed Stoneface, starred in *The Navigator* and *The General*? **Buster Keaton**

5. Who wrote *The White Peacock* and *The Plumed Serpent*? **D H Lawrence**

6. Which wading bird's cry is called a boom? **The bittern's**

7. Which island had HMS *Bounty* just left when the crew mutinied? **Tahiti**

8. Which black singer was known as The Mother of the Blues? **Ma Rainey**

9. Which stretch of water does the west end of the England/Scotland border run into? **Solway Firth**

10. In which county are the towns of Maryport, Wigton and Egremement? **Cumbria**

11. Where did John Brown try to capture an arsenal in 1859? **Harper's Ferry**

12. Which common cage-bird is sometimes called the Australian love-bird? **Budgerigar**

13. What is Bordeaux Mixture? Is it a blend of tobacco, a wine, an insecticide or a type of tea? **Insecticide**

14. What are Crambo and Dumb Crambo? **Games**

15. Which country forms the southern coast of the Black Sea? **Turkey**

16. Edward of Woodstock, Earl of Chester and Prince of Wales, died in 1376. By what name is he better known? **The Black Prince**

17. Of what tree is the Highland Games caber usually made? **Larch**

18. Where in Canada is an annual attraction called the Stampede held? **Calgary**

19. In the Bible, who denied Jesus thrice before the cock crowed twice? **Peter**

20. Who took *Boom Bang-a-Bang* to No 2 in the charts in 1969? **Lulu**

Quiz 130

1. Which one word means a hole-making tool, a blow and a mixed beverage? **Punch**

2. What did S stand for in the monetary abbreviation LSD? **Solidi**

3. At which theatre has *The Mousetrap* been performed since 1974? **St Martin's**

4. In which TV series was John Forsythe heard but never seen? ***Charlie's Angels***

5. In which athletic event was Joyce Smith particularly renowned? **Marathon**

6. Which actress married Don Johnson twice? **Melanie Griffith**

7. Whose Top Ten hits include *Kingston Town*, *Homely Girl* and *Higher Ground*? **UB40's**

8. Who played the female lead in the films *Teacher's Pet*, *That Touch of Mink* and *Move Over Darling*? **Doris Day**

9. Which game is played by the Calgary Flames, Pittsburgh Penguins and New York Rangers? **Ice hockey**

10. By what name did Marie Groscholtz become famous? Was she Madame Curie, Marie Lloyd or Madame Tussaud? **Madame Tussaud**

11. If you had a samisen would you wear it, play it or eat it? **Play it**

12. Which famous monument was designed by William Railton and finally built in 1842? **Nelson's Column**

13. Is Tree Ear a disease of monkeys, a mushroom or a parasitic plant? **A mushroom**

14. Who wrote the poems *The Pied Piper of Hamelin* and *Home Thoughts From Abroad*? **Robert Browning**

15. Polly Peachum and Lucy Lockit appear in which opera by John Gay? ***The Beggar's Opera***

16. True or false: Victoria is the capital of the Seychelles? **True**

17. How many wickets did Jim Laker take in the 1956 Old Trafford Test Match? **19**

18. What is inspected with an otoscope? **The ear**

19. Whose novels included *Tortilla Flat* and *The Moon Is Down*? **John Steinbeck's**

20. What creature was cartoon character Chilly Willy? **A penguin**

Quiz 131

1. For whom did Clarence House become home in 1953? **The Queen Mother**

2. When did a hesternal event occur? **Yesterday**

3. Is a frigatoon a ship, a bird or a type of bean? **A ship**

4. Who designed the Royal Pavilion, Brighton? **John Nash**

5. Tom Morris and his son between them won which title 8 times? **British Open Golf**

6. What was the name of the dance troupe in *Kenny Everett's Video Show*? **Hot Gossip**

7. Which Anglo-Saxon kingdom was ruled by Offa? **Mercia**

8. What was the surname of the brothers Dante Gabriel, William Michael and their sister Christina? **Rossetti**

9. Whose Top Ten hits included *Enjoying the Silence*, *I Feel You* and *In Your Room*? **Depeche Mode**

10. Torticollis is an abnormality which affects which part of the body? **Neck [accept head]**

11. In what year did Roger Bannister run the first sub-four minute mile? **1954**

12. True or false: Hans Arp, Alexander Calder and Alberto Giacometti were all famous painters? **False (Sculptors)**

13. Which famous person was born at Domremy in France in 1412? **Joan of Arc**

14. Who was the jewel thief in the first *Pink Panther* film? **The Phantom**

15. Prince Aly Khan married which fim star? **Rita Hayworth**

16. Whose last words were: "You will show my head to the people. It is well worthwhile."? Danton, Walter Raleigh or Lady Jane Grey? **Danton**

17. Shotts and Dykehead Caledonian have been World Champion . . . (what) many times? **Pipe Band**

18. Who played the title role in the 1995 film *Judge Dredd*? **Sylvester Stallone**

19. Who wrote the play *The Cherry Orchard*? **Chekhov**

20. Who had a 1964 hit with *Um Um Um Um Um Um*? **Wayne Fontana and The Mindbenders**

Quiz 132

1. Which of these was NEVER Footballer of the Year: Kenny Burns, Billy Bremner or Denis Law? **Denis Law**

2. Which Scottish region has the same name as a musical instrument? **Fife**

3. What is the main seasoning in Hungarian Goulash? **Paprika**

4. Which school was the first to have an old school tie? **Eton**

5. Who played Capstick in the TV series *Capstick's Law*? **William Gaunt**

6. What was the middle name of King Gillette, inventor of the disposable razor blade? Was it Sharp, Camp or Candy? **Camp**

7. In which army of ancient times were the elite troops known as Ten Thousand Immortals? **Persian army**

8. True or false: film star Shirley Temple became a US ambassador? **True**

9. Who was fatally shot as he passed the Texas School Book Depository? **John F Kennedy**

10. When did Harold Wilson retire as Prime Minister? **1976**

11. The Piccard brothers were famous what in the 1930s? **Balloonists**

12. J Fletcher-Dodd founded the first what at Caister-On-Sea in 1906? **Holiday Camp**

13. In which TV series did Pauline Collins and John Alderton play townies who moved to a Gloucestershire village? ***Forever Green***

14. Who married Princess Yashara before searching for enlightenment? **Buddha**

15. In a famous novel, who defeated all Prince John's knights at a great tournament at Ashby-De-La-Zouche? **Ivanhoe**

16. Which classic film was promoted under the slogan: 'Don't give away the ending – it's the only one we have.'? ***Psycho***

17. Where, up to a hundred years ago, might you have seen the mottoes 'Let Love Increase', 'For ever and for aye', 'In Thee My Choice I Do Rejoice' and 'When this you see, then think of me'? **Inscribed in rings**

18. Which opera is set on Catfish Row? ***Porgy and Bess***

19. Which former World Heavyweight Boxing Champion was wounded in the airborne invasion of Crete in 1941? **Max Schmeling**

20. Which one word means reasons or motives, coffee dregs and private enclosed land? **Grounds**

Quiz 133

1. Of which Scottish football manager was it said: "His problem is that he thinks tactics are a brand of peppermint."? **Ally MacLeod**

2. In which biographical film did Dustin Hoffman portray an infamous comedian? ***Lenny***

3. What relation was Napoleon III of France to Napoleon Bonaparte? **Nephew**

4. What word fits these definitions: a backless slipper, a type of spinning jenny and the offspring of a he-ass and a mare? **Mule**

5. What is écarté? **A card game**

6. Rondeau and rondel are two types of what? **Poem**

7. Thorp is an old word for what? **Village or hamlet**

8. When traditionally are simnel cakes made? **Mid Lent or Easter**

9. Which team did Bill Nicholson manage? **Tottenham Hotspur**

10. The First Triumvirate consisted of Julius Caesar, Crassus and who? **Pompey**

11. Who had No 1 hits with *Why?* and *Do You Mind* in 1960? **Anthony Newley**

12. Which word, believed to come from RAF slang, means a mischievous spirit which causes damage? **Gremlin**

13. What is the musical term for a flourish performed by a solo instrument at the close of a movement? **Cadenza**

14. What is the Javanese method of putting designs on cloth using wax and dye? **Batik**

15. Which International Athletics competition was first held in 1968 in Chicago? **The Special Olympics**

16. In old slang, what was 'quod'? **Prison**

17. What sort of creature is a killdeer? **A bird**

18. The adjective saurian means 'like a . . . (what)'? **Lizard**

19. According to the Premium Bonds prospectus, where are the serial numbers of winning bonds published? **In the *London Gazette***

20. Where does a hamster carry grain and seeds? **In its cheeks**

Quiz 134

1. What does an ichthyophagist do? **Eats fish**

2. Which game was invented in India in 1875 and reached England ten years later? **Snooker**

3. Is cassata a type of mortar, pasta or ice-cream? **Ice-cream**

4. In which country did Guy Gibson die? **Holland**

5. Which is the only bird in the Chinese calendar? **Rooster**

6. Who had a No 1 hit in 1974 with *Billy Don't Be A Hero*? **Paper Lace**

7. What is breccia? Is it a type of moss, a kind of rock or seaweed? **A kind of rock**

8. Which country has the shortest coastline? **Monaco**

9. In which TV series did Ralph Waite play the father of a big family? ***The Waltons***

10. In which country was President Allende overthrown by General Pinochet? **Chile**

11. In which sport would you use a trudgen? **Swimming**

12. True or false: a wapacut is a species of eagle? **False (It is an owl.)**

13. In which building are the Promenade Concerts now held? **Royal Albert Hall**

14. Who had a No 1 hit with *China In Your Hand*? **T'Pau**

15. According to tradition, Bonnie Prince Charlie gave Captain McKinnon the recipe for which liqueur? **Drambuie**

16. Which postal item was copyrighted by J P Charlton in 1861? **Postcard**

17. Which religious movement, founded in 1872, was originally called the International Bible Students? **Jehovah's Witnesses**

18. In sport, which game has the largest playing pitch? **Polo**

19. Which song, popular with both sides in World War 2, was written by Hans Leip, a German soldier in World War 1? ***Lili Marlene***

20. The Kit-Cat Club, founded in London in 1700, took its name from something that was served there. Was it mutton pies, chocolate cake or iced coffee? **Mutton Pies**

Quiz 135

1. What fires a SLBM? **Submarine**

2. The Hapsburgs, the Austrian Royal family, were renowned for a certain physical characteristic. What was it? **The lip (or lower jaw)**

3. In physics, for what is Hare's apparatus used? **To compare or find densities of liquids**

4. Who would carry out bosing: a brewer, an archaeologist or a sign painter? **Archaeologist**

5. Michael Ostrog, Kosminski, M J Druitt and J K Stephen were all suspected of being whom? **Jack the Ripper**

6. Who wrote the poems *Locksley Hall*, *Maud* and *The Idylls of the King*? **Tennyson**

7. What is the capital of Colombia? **Bogota**

8. True or false: Indian Ink originally came from China? **True**

9. To an Australian, what are strides? **Trousers**

10. In equestrianism, which event tests the horse's obedience? **Dressage**

11. Which of the *Road To* films was set in the Klondike Gold Rush? ***Road To Utopia***

12. What was originally known as the Pari Mutuel? **The Tote**

13. What does the Trachtenberg System involve? **Mathematical calculations**

14. Which European city is known as The Bride of the Sea? **Venice**

15. What is matze? Is it Jewish bread, Japanese fishcakes or Polish sausage? **Jewish bread**

16. Which flower was nicknamed 'Kiss-behind-the-garden-gate'? **Pansy**

17. Who had Top Ten hits with *Heaven Must be Missing an Angel* and *Whodunnit*? **Tavares**

18. In America, what is a cayuse? **A horse**

19. Who presented the TV gameshow *Midas Touch*? **Bradley Walsh**

20. Buck-and-wing and soft-shoe were early forms of which style of dancing? **Tap dancing**

Quiz 136

1. Which actor produced the Whitehall farces in the 1950s and 1960s? **Brian Rix**

2. Who said: "I'm sure I was wrong on a number of occasions, but I can't think of anything immediately."? **Margaret Thatcher**

3. For what is bhp the abbreviation? **Brake horse-power**

4. In poetry, who roams the Gromboolian plain looking for his Jumbly Girl with the sky blue hands? **The Dong (with the luminous nose)**

5. In what field were Jutus Liebig, Harold Urey and Richard Kuhn famous? **Chemistry**

6. Who played the title role in the film *The Elephant Man*? **John Hurt**

7. Which was the only full-scale naval battle of World War 1? **Battle of Jutland**

8. With what was Morton's Fork concerned? Was it road-building, taxation or gardening? **Taxation**

9. Where is the HQ of the World Health Organisation? **Geneva**

10. Who wrote *Lords and Ladies* and *Small Gods*? **Terry Pratchett**

11. Fermin Cacho won the 1992 Olympic 1500 metres. Give his nationality. **Spanish**

12. In the TV series *Telford's Change*, what was Telford's job? **Bank manager**

13. When the witches chased Tam O'Shanter, what did they get? **His horse's tail**

14. Rococo and Baroque are styles of what? **Architecture**

15. Who had Top Ten hits with *Me the Peaceful Heart*, *Leave a Little Love* and *The Man Who Sold the World*? **Lulu**

16. Who are in charge in a theocracy? **Priests**

17. Which sea is connected to the Baltic Sea by the Kiel Canal? **North Sea**

18. What would happen if you took an emetic medicine? **You'd vomit**

19. Which Prime Minister was the Earl of Chatham? **William Pitt**

20. True or false: *The Modern Prometheus* was the subtitle of the novel *Dracula*? **False (It was the subtitle of *Frankenstein*.)**

Quiz 137

1. Proverbially, what do late workers burn? **The midnight oil**

2. Which day follows Shrove Tuesday? **Ash Wednesday**

3. Under which name was Luke McMasters a professional wrestler? **Giant Haystacks**

4. A 3,000 year old bas-relief was sold for $11 million in 1994. Where had it been for many years: in a cow shed, a school tuckshop or a garden? **School tuckshop**

5. Who wrote the song *Moon River*? **Henry Mancini**

6. Which puppet series sprang out of *Sesame Street*? ***The Muppet Show***

7. Experiments to prove the earth was flat or otherwise were carried out in 1838 and 1870 at the Old Bedford Level. What was the Old Bedford Level? **A canal**

8. In the sci-fi film *Them*, what were 'them'? **Giant ants**

9. Who would have practised his skill on a quintain? **A (Mounted) Knight**

10. In which sport are there events called The Hambletonian and Little Brown Jug? **Harness Racing**

11. Who are thespians? **Actors**

12. Who had a No 1 with *Doctorin' the Tardis*? **Timelords**

13. Who wrote *The Scorpio Illusion* and *The Road To Omaha*? **Robert Ludlum**

14. Give the name of Alistair Cooke's long-running weekly radio talk on the BBC. ***Letter From America***

15. With which sport is Clare Francis associated? **Sailing**

16. True or false: Laurence Sterne created a character called Tristram Shandy? **True**

17. What was the name of Queen Victoria's residence on the Isle of Wight? **Osborne House**

18. What kind of fish is a hammerhead? **Shark**

19. Who wears a chasuble? Is it a priest, a knight in armour or a diver? **A priest**

20. David Duckham, Mervyn Davies and Tony Ward were all voted Player of the Year in the 1970s in which sport? **Rugby**

Quiz 138

1. Which school film had the theme music *Rock Around the Clock*? **Blackboard Jungle**

2. In which profession was Nelson Mandela qualified? **Legal (Lawyer)**

3. Who came second when Ronald Reagan was first elected US president? **Jimmy Carter**

4. Who played the lead – a canal lock-keeper – in the TV series *The River*? **David Essex**

5. In which county is Skegness? **Lincolnshire**

6. Who wrote *Rodney Stone*, *The White Company* and *The Lost World*? **Sir Arthur Conan Doyle**

7. Who was Prime Minister when World War 1 started? **Herbert Asquith**

8. Traditionally, the word 'lascar' was used to describe Indians doing what job? **Sailors**

9. Which religious order was founded by Ignatius Loyola? **Jesuits**

10. Which product was advertised on TV by Sharon Maughan and Anthony Head? **Gold Blend Coffee**

11. In which book of the Bible is the story of Samson? Is it Deuteronomy, Joshua or Judges? **Judges**

12. True or false: bonny-clabber is a type of cloth? **False (It is a drink.)**

13. Who played Conan in the films *Conan the Barbarian* and *Conan the Destroyer*? **Arnold Schwarzenegger**

14. Which Prime Minister resigned as a result of the Suez crisis? **Anthony Eden**

15. What exactly is a chow-chow? **A dog**

16. Opium, Californian and Yellow Horned are all varieties of which flower? **Poppy**

17. Which Frenchwoman won the Wimbledon Ladies Singles five times in succession in the 1920s? **Suzanne Lenglen**

18. Which river is known as the King of Waters? **Amazon**

19. Who composed the orchestral suites *London*, *London Again* and *From Meadow to Mayfair*? **Eric Coates**

20. Who is the Queen's representative in each county? **Lord Lieutenant**

Quiz 139

1. Which ruler was assassinated by his own guards in 41 AD? **Caligula**

2. Who played the female lead in the film *Out of Africa*? **Meryl Streep**

3. Razorbills, puffins and guillemots belong to which family of birds? **Auks**

4. Who had a 1985 No 1 with *Nineteen*? **Paul Hardcastle**

5. Who composed the oratorios *Samson*, *Belshazzar* and *Judas Maccabeus*? **Handel**

6. Who led the Hot Five and Hot Seven jazz bands in the 1920s? **Louis Armstrong**

7. Alpha acid gives a bitter taste to what? **Beer**

8. True or false: Likud is an Israeli political party? **True**

9. Where in Britain is the Jorvik Viking Centre? **York**

10. On TV, who presented *Don't Forget Your Toothbrush*? **Chris Evans**

11. In which sport were Matt Biondi, Jeff Rouse and Melvin Stewart all World Champions? **Swimming**

12. What is long staple? **A type of cotton**

13. Which Protestant leader of the sixteenth century clashed with Mary I of England and Mary, Queen of Scots? **John Knox**

14. Which natural disaster struck the Philippines in 1976, Indonesia in 1979 and Japan in 1983? **A tsunami (tidal wave)**

15. At which 1346 battle was the power of the English longbow first demonstrated? **Crécy**

16. Which musical note value is equal to two crotchets? **Minim**

17. Which drink was advertised by a poster showing it halfway down an ostrich's throat while a zookeeper looked on in dismay? **Guinness**

18. What is the Latin name for the sword lily? Is it galanthus, gladiolus or iris? **Gladiolus**

19. In religion, what does the symbol of marked doorposts and lintel signify? **The Passover**

20. Which famous Englishman's will left his wife only his 'second best bed'? **Shakespeare's**

Quiz 140

1. Who had Top Ten hits with *Sweetest Smile* and *Wonderful Life*? **Black**

2. Who wrote *The Road To Lichfield*, *Moon Tiger* and *City of the Mind*? **Penelope Lively**

3. Who wrote the operas *Tristan and Isolde* and *Lohengrin*? **Wagner**

4. True or false: a wallaroo is a species of kangaroo? **True**

5. Which English king had a dog named after him? **Charles II**

6. Which zoo had the first reptile house, first aquarium and first insect house? **London Zoo**

7. Where is the Bay of Rainbows and the Sea of Vapours? **On the moon**

8. Who had a 1979 No 1 hit with *Tragedy*? **Bee Gees**

9. In which cathedral is the Mappa Mundi kept? **Hereford**

10. In the 16th century, was Great Harry a bell, a gun or a warship? **A warship**

11. In which sport was Didier Auriol the 1994 World Champion? **Rally driving**

12. Who wrote *The Millstone*, *Jerusalem the Golden* and *The Ice Age*? **Margaret Drabble**

13. Who abide by Hart's Rules? Printers and publishers, horsebreeders or scientists? **Printers and publishers**

14. What was the subject of the TV programme *Rhodes Around Britain*? **Cookery**

15. Which musical film contained the songs *Tomorrow*, *Fat Sam's Grand Slam* and *So You Wanna Be a Boxer*? ***Bugsy Malone***

16. Which singer, famous for romantic songs such as *Goodnight Sweetheart*, *Love Is the Sweetest Thing* and *The Touch of Your Lips*, was killed in an air raid in 1941? **Al Bowlly**

17. What relation was Queen Victoria to George IV? **Niece**

18. Which lighthouse was kept by Grace Darling's father? **Longstone**

19. What's the official language of Haiti? **French**

20. True or false: there is a Theodore Roosevelt National Park? **True (In North Dakota)**

Quiz 141

1. Devil's Tower in Wyoming played an important part in which 1977 film? ***Close Encounters of the Third Kind***

2. Which one word means a unit of weight, an enclosure for animals and to beat? **Pound**

3. What was the nickname of actress Emily Charlotte Langtry? **Jersey Lily**

4. Which is the main trophy for eights won at Henley Royal Regatta? **Grand Challenge Cup**

5. Which Shakespearean character said: "I'll put a girdle round about the earth in forty minutes"? **Puck**

6. Who was the dizzy blonde who couldn't add up in the TV show *The Golden Shot*? **Anne Aston**

7. What was a Spanish worm: a hidden nail, a weevil in ship's biscuits or a poisonous snake? **A hidden nail**

8. True or false: Scott Joplin was the originator of boogie woogie? **False (He popularised ragtime.)**

9. What is a tench? **A fish**

10. Which is the largest of these islands: Zanzibar, Sri Lanka or Madagascar? **Madagascar**

11. Which game includes Mr Bun the Baker, his wife and children? **Happy Families**

12. Who played the male lead in Hitchcock's *Marnie*? **Sean Connery**

13. Which song, written by The Corries, has replaced *Scotland the Brave* as the unofficial Scottish national anthem at football and rugby matches? ***Flower of Scotland***

14. What cried out to warn the giant when it was stolen by Jack before he escaped down the beanstalk? **The Harp**

15. Which strip cartoon was drawn by Trog? ***Flook***

16. Name the Duke of Bedford's stately home. **Woburn Abbey**

17. What was the name of the woman in John Cleland's book *Memoirs of a Woman of Pleasure*? **Fanny Hill**

18. Who were the German husband and wife team who popularised underwater TV programmes in the 1950s and 1960s? **Hans and Lottie Hass**

19. Which unit of measurement was based on the distance from the elbow to the tip of the middle finger? **Cubit**

20. Anything 'napiform' is shaped like which vegetable? **Turnip**

Quiz 142

1. Into which river was Achilles plunged to make him invulnerable? **Styx**

2. Which is the largest Welsh county? **Dyfed**

3. Who was the first British martyr, who lived at Verulamium? **St Alban**

4. Who was No 1 in the charts with *West End Girls* in 1986? **Pet Shop Boys**

5. In medicine, with what does agmatology deal? **Fractures**

6. In literature, which group set out on a journey from The Tabard Inn in Southwark? **Chaucer's Pilgrims**

7. On which racecourse were the World War 2 Derby races run? **Newmarket**

8. Who wrote *Goodbye Mr Chips* and *Lost Horizon*? **James Hilton**

9. In which city is the Walker art gallery? **Liverpool**

10. Which film star's international career really took off with the 1956 film *And God Created Woman*? **Brigitte Bardot's**

11. What is the sum of the angles in a hexagon? **720**

12. On which peninsula are Spain and Portugal? **Iberian**

13. What is the legal expression for when a judge hears a case in private? ***In camera***

14. Who played the black drill sergeant in *An Officer and a Gentleman*? **Louis Gosset**

15. Which jazz musician wrote *Mood Indigo*, *Sophisticated Lady* and *Black and Tan Fantasy*? **Duke Ellington**

16. In which novel is a traveller made welcome by a race of small, beautiful and graceful people called the Eloi? ***The Time Machine***

17. The name of which Greek god is used to describe a handsome man or perfect specimen? **Adonis**

18. A sculpture entitled *Monument To the Equator* stands in the town of Guachala, in which country? **Ecuador**

19. In which ancient civilisation's literature was Man created by the god Marduk? **Babylonia's**

20. Who directed the 1995 film *Heat*? **Michael Mann**

Quiz 143

1. Which newspaper's headline on 4th May 1982 was "Gotcha!"? ***The Sun's***

2. Which restaurant guide was launched by Raymond Postgate in 1949? ***Good Food Guide***

3. Five countries provided most of the UN troops in Korea in the 1950s. USA, Britain and Australia were three. Name one of the other two. **Canada or Turkey**

4. Where is the Ideal Home Exhibition held? **Earl's Court**

5. Who had a No1 hit in 1988 with *Heaven Is a Place On Earth*? **Belinda Carlisle**

6. Who played Richard Hannay in the Hitchcock version of *The 39 Steps*? **Robert Donat**

7. What kind of creature was Robert Louis Stevenson's Modestine? **A donkey**

8. Which planes were used by the Dam Busters? **Lancasters**

9. In which sport did the Russian, Prince Oblensky, represent England? **Rugby Union**

10. What honorary title is given to the MP who has sat in the Commons for the longest uninterrupted period? **Father of the House**

11. Who played Apollo Creed in the *Rocky* movies? **Carl Weathers**

12. On TV, who played The Singing Detective? **Michael Gambon**

13. Which African country's capital is named after an American President? **Liberia**

14. Who played the male lead in the 1995 film *Loch Ness*? **Ted Danson**

15. Who founded the magazine *Time* and the pictorial weekly *Life*? **Henry Robinson Luce**

16. Which member of the Royal family married Marina of Greece in 1934? **Duke of Kent**

17. Who played Leslie Grantham's brother, a priest, in *The Paradise Club*? **Don Henderson**

18. Which county won the Cricket County Championship seven times in succession in the 1950s? **Surrey**

19. Which Commonwealth country has the ringgit as its unit of currency? **Malaysia**

20. Who won a gold medal for Britain in the 1960 Olympics for the 50 kilometre walk? **Don Thompson**

Quiz 144

1. In which English county was willow-pattern china created? **Staffordshire**

2. What would you keep in a cresset: flowers, fire, jewels or guns? **Fire**

3. Which vegetable is in the dish Egg Florentine? **Spinach**

4. In which sport is there a bonspiel? **Curling**

5. Which London theatre boasted "We never closed."? **Windmill**

6. Who sings the title song for the TV series *One Foot in the Grave*? **Eric Idle**

7. In which series of films was there a murderer named Michael Myles? **The *Halloween* films**

8. From which country do Moselle wines come? **Germany**

9. Which country's national anthem is called *The Peaceful Banks of the River Ipiranga*? **Brazil's**

10. What is a 'cryptogam'? Is it a code, a marine animal, a plant or an ancient monument? **A plant**

11. Who wrote *Joseph Andrews*, *Jonathan Wild* and *Tom Jones*? **Henry Fielding**

12. The French call it Lac Leman, the Germans Genfersee. What do we call it? **Lake Geneva**

13. Which former European country was ruled by the Hohenzollerns? **Prussia**

14. From which animal did Jenner develop his smallpox vaccine? **Cow**

15. Who was appointed head of the Spanish Inquisition in 1483? **Torquemada**

16. What is a mature horse below the height of fourteen and a half hands called? **A pony**

17. Who had Top Ten hits in the 1970s with *All Right Now*, *My Brother Jake* and *Wishing Well*? **Free**

18. From which language does the word 'ketchup' come? **Chinese**

19. Who composed the music for *A Fistful of Dollars, For a Few Dollars More* and *The Good, the Bad and the Ugly*? **Ennio Morricone**

20. In which country is November 2nd a National Holiday, celebrated as 'Day of the Dead'? **Mexico**

Quiz 145

1. In which war was the Battle of Inkerman? **Crimean**

2. Of which region in Italy is Rome the capital? **Latium (Lazio)**

3. Who published a book called *Stenographic Sound* in 1837? **Isaac Pitman**

4. Is a mammee a sea creature, a tree or a monkey? **A tree**

5. Which country won the European Song Contest with *A-Ba-Ni-Bi*? **Israel**

6. In which TV series did the Electric Mayhem Band appear? ***The Muppet Show***

7. Which royal princess died in 1982 after a car accident which her daughter survived? **Grace of Monaco**

8. In which novel is the title character hanged for the murder of the man to whom she bore an illegitimate child? **Tess of the D'Urbervilles**

9. Which word means an embarrassing position and a preserving liquid? **Pickle**

10. Whose Top Ten hits included *Stars* and *For Your Babies*? **Simply Red**

11. The Duke of Grafton, Marquess of Rockingham and Earl of Bute all held which position? **Prime Minister**

12. Where would you normally find a howdah? **On an elephant**

13. Who played Jesus in the film *The Last Temptation of Christ*? **Willem Dafoe**

14. Which actor and singer formed a band called King Crabbs? **Jimmy Nail**

15. In mythology, who was Actaeon? **A hunter**

16. True or false: the first metal aircraft was built by Messerschmitt? **False (Junkers)**

17. On what was Emily Post regarded as an authority? **Etiquette**

18. Which famous chocolate bar was available only to GIs during World War 2? **The Hershey Bar**

19. Which one word means an amateur radio operator, a bad actor and cured pigmeat? **Ham**

20. Bones found in a West Sussex quarry in 1993 led to archaeologists calling their owner what? **Boxgrove Man**

Quiz 146

1. Which actor played Mr Allison in *Heaven Knows, Mr Allison*? **Robert Mitchum**

2. On the stress scale, which rates highest: pregnancy, mortgage, moving home or retirement? **Retirement**

3. Which Oscar winning song came from the film *The Thomas Crown Affair*? ***Windmills of Your Mind***

4. Which Spanish painter painted the picture known as *The Rokeby Venus*? **Velasquez**

5. Which former Northern MP made a speech in the House of Lords on his 100th birthday? **Lord Shinwell**

6. What does a colporteur sell? **Religious books and tracts**

7. Where in Britain is the Up-Helly-Aa festivity held? **Shetlands**

8. The Cook Islands are an associated territory of which country? **New Zealand**

9. Who was the father of Alexander, Earl of Ulster? **Prince Richard, Duke of Gloucester**

10. Which ancient Greek word meant "I have found it!"? **Eureka**

11. How did the scientist Pierre Curie die? **Run over by a cart**

12. The acre was originally a strip of land one furlong by one . . . (what)? **Chain**

13. True or false: a kit was a small violin? **True**

14. What colour light do ships display at night on the starboard side? **Green**

15. Which fruit is the favourite of the orang-utan? Is it mango, pawpaw or durian? **Durian**

16. Who chose Ottawa to be the capital of Canada? **Queen Victoria**

17. Which part of London took its name from ornamental collars which were once made there? Was it Piccadilly, Holborn or Berkeley Square? **Piccadilly**

18. What travels the 'mean free path'? **A molecule**

19. In which city in 1819 did the Peterloo Massacre take place? **Manchester**

20. Who wrote the operettas *Rose Marie* and *The Vagabond King*? **Rudolf Friml**

Quiz 147

1. Who had Top Ten hits with *Touch Me*, *Do Ya Do Ya* and *Nothing's Gonna Stop Me Now*? **Samantha Fox**

2. Who was Mr Universe from 1968 to 1970? **Arnold Schwarzenegger**

3. Which country did Josef Barthel, Olympic Gold medallist in the 1952 1500 metres, represent? **Luxembourg**

4. True or false: Eva Peron was once President of Argentina? **False**

5. In which country did the Mau Mau terrorists operate? **Kenya**

6. Is pishogue a canoe, a rich stew or sorcery? **Sorcery**

7. In which country is the opera *Turandot* set? Is it Germany, Spain or China? **China**

8. What name was given to the American patriots who were ready to fight at a moment's notice in the period immediately before the War of Independence? **Minutemen**

9. On TV, what was the name of the company founded by Reggie Perrin? **Grot**

10. In tic-tac, what does a hand on the head indicate? **Number One**

11. A Virginian farmer, first name Charles, inflicted instant punishment on wrongdoers in the 18th and 19th centuries. His surname became which word in the English language? **Lynch**

12. Whose statue is thought to have inspired Shelley's poem that begins "My name is Ozymandias": was it Tutankhamun's, Rameses II's or Akhenaton's? **Rameses II's**

13. Which of his films did Hitchcock remake more than 20 years later? ***The Man Who Knew Too Much***

14. Words ending in 'mancy' have to do with what? **Fortune-telling, divination**

15. Which name does Viola assume in her male disguise in *Twelfth Night*? **Cesario**

16. Which Nobel Prize was won by Andrei Sakharov in 1975? **Peace**

17. What was the Village People's only No 1? ***YMCA***

18. Which play by A A Milne was a dramatised version of *The Wind in the Willows*? ***Toad of Toad Hall***

19. Which word means to pull sharply, a stupid person or to cut and dry beef? **Jerk**

20. True or false: John Bunyan was originally a farmer? **False (He was a tinker.)**

Quiz 148

1. Which of these is NOT a lizard: chuckwalla, slowworm, gelada, agama? **Gelada (monkey)**

2. 'Izzard' is an old word for which letter of the alphabet? **Z**

3. In craps, if you throw a total of four, what should you throw next to win? **4**

4. What is the popular name for the painful spasmodic contraction of a muscle? **Cramp**

5. What was the nickname of the folk and blues singer Huddie Leadbetter? **Leadbelly**

6. Who had a No 1 hit in 1981 with *Don't You Want Me*? **Human League**

7. What would you drink in the cha-no-yu? **Tea (Tea ceremony)**

8. Complete this quintet: Manhattan, Brooklyn, Bronx, Richmond and . . . **Queens**

9. Which one word means a couple, to bind or tie close and to fill with energy? **Brace**

10. Which famous book was compiled by Henry Baker with William Monk in 1861? ***Hymns Ancient and Modern***

11. What name is given to metals that don't tarnish in air or water and have good resistance to acids? **Noble**

12. On TV, who played Kavanagh QC? **John Thaw**

13. Which is the largest lake in Wales? **Lake Bala**

14. Which expression for a devoted couple originates in a 1735 poem? **Darby and Joan**

15. Which international organisation was set up after World War 1 with the purpose of achieving world peace? **League of Nations**

16. What is a duppy? Is it a tropical fish, a ghost or a rock plant? **A ghost**

17. Titania, Oberon, Miranda and Ariel are all moons of which planet? **Uranus**

18. What connects Mrs Tiggywinkle, an Arthur Lowe TV series and a wasp which builds nests of clay? **Potter**

19. In which novel does Angela Quested accuse a local doctor of rape? ***A Passage To India***

20. Which film idol was attacked in the press as a 'painted pansy'? **Rudolph Valentino**

Quiz 149

1. To which Biblical event does the adjective 'diluvial' refer? **The Flood**

2. Which river did Julius Caesar cross and, by doing so, cause a civil war? **Rubicon**

3. In which country did Louis Riel lead a rebellion and set up a provisional government in 1869? **Canada**

4. Who starred in the films *Monkey Business*, *Houseboat*, *Indiscreet* and *Walk, Don't Run*? **Cary Grant**

5. Whose army spent a dreadful winter in 1777-78 at Valley Forge? **George Washington's**

6. In which country is Valparaiso an important port? **Chile**

7. In Henry III's reign, compurgation was introduced and was the forerunner of what? **The Jury System**

8. What is ars antiqua? **A musical style**

9. Who was principal conductor of the Hallé Orchestra from 1949 to 1970? **Sir John Barbirolli**

10. Which actress first played Miss Marple on TV in 1984? **Joan Hickson**

11. What colour is a giraffe's tongue? **Blue**

12. Which sides fought the battle of Cold Harbour? **Union and Confederates (American Civil War)**

13. In Greek mythology, who descended to the underworld to retrieve his wife, Eurydice? **Orpheus**

14. Arch, whorl and loops are all parts of what? **Fingerprints**

15. Up to which date do we mean when the English language is referred to as 'Old English'? **1150**

16. Who were Patti, Maxine and Laverne? **The Andrews Sisters**

17. Which is the most poisonous fish in the world? Is it the pearlfish, stonefish, lionfish or needlefish? **Stonefish**

18. What is the chief food of baby whales? **Their mother's milk**

19. What is known as the Universal Solvent? **Water**

20. Who was the first Englishman to be killed flying an aeroplane? **Charles Rolls**

Quiz 150

1. Sun, spectacled, brown and sloth are all species of what? **Bear**

2. Bayern is the German name for which region of Germany? **Bavaria**

3. True or false: December 25th is not a Saint's Day? **True**

4. In what sphere was Karsh of Ottawa famous? **Photography**

5. Who played Mel Gibson's partner in the *Lethal Weapon* films? **Danny Glover**

6. Of which African country was Flight Lieutenant Jerry Rawlings leader? **Ghana**

7. Which style of music is associated with the Dixie Hummingbirds, Swan Silvertones and Five Blind Boys of Alabama? **Gospel Music**

8. Which British commander was so popular during the Seven Years War that many inns and pubs were named after him? **Marquis of Granby**

9. Which country in 1958 introduced an economic policy called the Great Leap Forward? **China**

10. Which country do you associate with a guerilla group called the Tamil Tigers? **Sri Lanka**

11. Who was the first jockey to win the English Derby *and* the Kentucky Derby? **Steve Cauthen**

12. In ancient Greece, what was a hoplite? **A soldier**

13. Who, in 1995, produced an album called *No Need To Argue*? **The Cranberries**

14. Who presented the TV series *Alphabet of Britain*? **Lucinda Lambton**

15. Fohn, Khamsin, Brickfielder and Harmattan are all types of . . . (what)? **Winds**

16. Who said: "This is the greatest week in the history of the world since the creation."? **Richard Nixon**

17. In which county is Jodrell Bank? **Cheshire**

18. Whose poetry anthologies include *The North Ship*, *The Whitsun Weddings* and *High Windows*? **Philip Larkin's**

19. Who said of his conversion: "I felt my heart strangely warmed. I felt I did trust in Christ alone for salvation, and an assurance was given me that He had taken away my sins."? **John Wesley**

20. For which event was the first English commemorative medal struck? **Defeat of the Armada**

Quiz 151

1. What would you do in a Cambio? **Exchange money**

2. What is a water moccasin? **A snake**

3. Who on TV appears as Alan Partridge and Paul Calf? **Steve Coogan**

4. Against which disease was the Salk vaccine developed? **Polio**

5. Kelts, alevins and grilse are all forms of what? **Salmon**

6. What is produced by placing a fodder crop in an airtight structure and letting it ferment? **Silage (Ensilage)**

7. What sort of writings would you associate with Raphael Holinshed? **History**

8. Which English bowler took 9 wickets in an innings against South Africa in 1994? **Devon Malcolm**

9. Which country had a parliament called the Duma? **Russia**

10. What was a psaltery? Was it a musical instrument, a book of psalms or a medicinal herb? **A musical instrument**

11. Which Spaniard founded the city of Lima? **Francisco Pizarro**

12. Which Scottish football player was sent home from the 1978 World Cup for taking drugs? **Willie Johnstone**

13. In pickles, what are gherkins? **Cucumbers**

14. Which country is Mexico's largest southern border neighbour? **Guatemala**

15. Who wrote *A Handful of Dust*, *Vile Bodies* and *Decline and Fall*? **Evelyn Waugh**

16. Which of these is not a London Men's Club: Boodles, Forum, Carlton? **Forum**

17. Which Briton was World Motor racing Champion in 1962 and 1968? **Graham Hill**

18. In which film was Dustin Hoffman 121 years old? ***Little Big Man***

19. In Japan, what is No? **A type of theatre**

20. In which year was Lady Jane Grey queen? **1553**

Quiz 152

1. Which country's Prime Minister was apparently drowned in 1967? **Australia's**

2. Where did the Allies first cross the Rhine in World War 2? **Remagen**

3. Which creature gets its name from the Spanish for lizard? **Alligator**

4. What is the principal female singer in an opera called? **Prima Donna**

5. Apart from a toothbrush, what else did the audience bring along in *Don't Forget Your Toothbrush*? **Passport**

6. How many players are there in a hurling team? **15**

7. Who was the incurable optimist in *David Copperfield*? **Mr Micawber**

8. In which field of science would you encounter the Pons Asinorum? **Geometry**

9. Which meat was used in a Woolton pie? **None**

10. In which Gilbert and Sullivan operetta does Pooh Bah appear? ***The Mikado***

11. According to the Talmud, what did God do with seven handfuls of earth brought to him by the angel Azrael? **He made Adam**

12. Which Duke's seat is Badminton? **Duke of Beaufort's**

13. Which beaten boxer said to his wife in 1926: "Honey, I forgot to duck"? **Jack Dempsey**

14. Which White House room is the President's office? **Oval Room**

15. Who played Dr Watson to Basil Rathbone's Sherlock Holmes? **Nigel Bruce**

16. Which country built the Mannerheim Line as a defence against Russia? **Finland**

17. Which doctor's suicide note in 1963 said : "I am sorry to disappoint the vultures."? **Stephen Ward's**

18. Who wrote the novel *Kipps*? **H G Wells**

19. Which drink's advertising slogan was "It's the real thing"? **Coca Cola's**

20. Which US general was granted an honorary knighthood by the Queen in 1991? **Norman Schwarzkopf**

Quiz 153

1. From which vegetable does ravioli take its name? **Turnip**

2. Who played the detective Anna Lee on TV? **Imogen Stubbs**

3. For whom did Nikki Lauda drive when he won the World Championship in 1975 and 1977? **Ferrari**

4. What is the name of the toy where a piece of wood shaped like two cones joined at their points is spun on a cord attached to two sticks? **Diabolo**

5. Who wrote the poems *Annabel Lee*, *The Bells* and *The Haunted Palace*? **Edgar Allan Poe**

6. Who wrote the musicals *Sweeney Todd* and *Sunday in the Park With George*? **Stephen Sondheim**

7. What is the Whispering Arrow? Is it a US fighter plane, a German train or a Japanese jetfoil? **A German train**

8. In legend, where did Joseph of Arimathea's staff take root and bud and now flowers every Christmas? **Glastonbury**

9. Who played the butler/valet, Hobson, in the film *Arthur*? **John Gielgud**

10. Up to the nineteenth century, where did a dog-whipper work? **In church**

11. Which animals were once called 'foul martens'? **Polecats**

12. True or false: there is an Ivory Wedding Anniversary? **True (14 years)**

13. Whose companions were turned into swine by the sorceress Circe? **Ulysses**

14. A hot drink of rum and water mixed with beaten eggs has the same name as which cartoon characters? **Tom and Jerry**

15. What does a deltiologist study and collect? **Postcards**

16. Whose novels have included *Secrets of the Morning* and *Dawn*? **Virginia Andrews**

17. In the Middle Ages, of what would a person be guilty if he had B branded on his forehead? **Blasphemy**

18. Which unlikely person played a missionary in the film *Shanghai Surprise*? **Madonna**

19. Who beat David Gower's English test runs record in 1993? **Graham Gooch**

20. Which French expression means 'so much the worse'? **Tant pis**

Quiz 154

1. Who composed the operas *The Bartered Bride* and *Dalibor*: was it Smetana, Schoenberg or Stockhausen? **Smetana**

2. Ganymede is the largest moon of which planet? **Jupiter**

3. Which US submarine crossed the North Pole under the ice in 1958? **USS *Nautilus***

4. Which leader was painted 'warts and all' by Samuel Cooper? **Oliver Cromwell**

5. In which TV drama series did Hale and Pace play policemen? ***A Pinch of Snuff***

6. Who had a sword called Arondight? **Lancelot**

7. Whose albums include *Tupelo Honey*, *Veedon Fleece* and *Hymns To the Silence*? **Van Morrison's**

8. True or false: the first steam tractor was built in 1769? **True**

9. For what does the abbreviation BOT stand? **Board of Trade**

10. What is the capital of Chile? **Santiago**

11. Whose album, *One Woman – The Ultimate Collection*, was a 1993 bestseller? **Diana Ross's**

12. What are you trying to catch if you sniggle? **Eels**

13. Which creatures are affected by a disease called the strangles? **Horses**

14. Which is the largest city in Switzerland? **Zurich**

15. Whose voice was the baby's thoughts in *Look Who's Talking*? **Bruce Willis's**

16. Vitamin B2 is also known as thiamin, folic acid or riboflavin? **Riboflavin**

17. What would you carry or keep in a wardian? **(Delicate) Plants**

18. Which people's work was dramatised in the TV series *The Knock*? **Customs and Excise**

19. What are you if you are 'au courant'? **Fully informed, up to date**

20. Which unit of measurement is equal to 3.2616 light years? **Parsec**

Quiz 155

1. Is Venus's Looking-Glass a type of quartz, a Cumbrian lake or a plant? **A plant**

2. Who wrote *A Connecticut Yankee in King Arthur's Court*? **Mark Twain**

3. What is a tocsin? **An alarm bell**

4. True or false: béchamel is a kind of caramel? **False (It is a white sauce.)**

5. In what sphere was Jean Muir famous? **Fashion**

6. Where is the Verrazano Narrows Bridge? **New York**

7. Where would you use a dongle? **On a computer**

8. Which Queen of Carthage loved Aeneas? **Dido**

9. Whose albums included *Natty Dread* and *Exodus*? **Bob Marley's**

10. Which vehicle took its common name from the fact that it was made to be used for general purposes? **Jeep**

11. In which TV series did Russ Abbot play Ted Fenwick? ***September Song***

12. To which country do the Azores belong? **Portugal**

13. Which Alice Walker novel, made into a 1985 film, won the Pulitzer prize? ***The Color Purple***

14. Who was the father of Henry IV? Was it Henry III, John of Gaunt or the Black Prince? **John of Gaunt**

15. For what is Gregory Powder used? **As a laxative, purgative**

16. Who played Captain Hook in the film *Hook*? **Dustin Hoffman**

17. Where is the Keck telescope? Is it in Bonn, Hawaii or Cambridge? **Hawaii**

18. In which country is Thunder Bay? Canada, New Zealand or Iceland? **Canada**

19. Port Moresby is the capital of which Commonwealth country? **Papua New Guinea**

20. True or false: Samarium is a chemical element? **True**

Quiz 156

1. On the Skull and Crossbones flag, what kind of bones are the crossbones? **Femurs**

2. Who wrote *Samson Agonistes*? **John Milton**

3. Who slew the monster Grendel in an old poem? **Beowulf**

4. If one, two and three are Cardinal, what are first, second and third? **Ordinal**

5. Which flower is sometimes called the Lent Lily? **Daffodil**

6. The colour of what in China indicated a mandarin's rank? **The button on his hat**

7. Who had Top Ten hits in the 1980s with *System Addict*, *Find the Time* and *Rain or Shine*? **Five Star**

8. In the 1960s, which London street was the fashion centre for the young? **Carnaby Street**

9. What did you do if you took the King's shilling? **Joined the army**

10. Who interpreted the writing on the wall? **Daniel**

11. To what did the expression "lock, stock and barrel" originally refer? **A gun**

12. Who in 1993 became the highest scoring Test batsman of all time? **Alan Border**

13. Was Angel Beast an old card game, a foodstuff or a cosmetic? **A card game**

14. For what is the Athenian, Draco, remembered? **Harsh laws**

15. During which war was the New Model Army formed? **English Civil War**

16. Who played the black film detective Shaft? **Richard Roundtree**

17. Who wrote the novel *The Card*? **Arnold Bennett**

18. Who said: "The lion and the calf shall lie down together, but the calf won't get much sleep."? **Woody Allen**

19. Who was the first US President to be awarded the Nobel Peace Prize (1906)? **Theodore Roosevelt**

20. In a famous children's book what was Cedric Errol's title? **Lord Fauntleroy**

Quiz 157

1. What was the Beatle's first UK No 1 hit? **From Me To You**

2. In the art medium tempera, what is mixed with powdered paint? **Egg yolk**

3. What connects these books: *Mein Kampf*, *Pilgrim's Progress* and *History of the World*? **All (partly) written in prison**

4. Which was the first American city to host the Olympics (1904)? **St Louis**

5. In which Shakespeare play do Beatrice and Benedick appear? ***Much Ado About Nothing***

6. What did General Wade construct in the Highlands from 1724 to 1730? **Roads**

7. What was the original ominous name for the Driver's Safety Device on electric and diesel trains? **Dead Man's Handle**

8. To where in Berkshire did CND march from London annually for many years? **Aldermaston**

9. Where did the Germans defeat the Russians over the 26th-30th August in 1914? **Tannenburg**

10. In which city did the Phoenix Park murders occur in 1882? **Dublin**

11. Chelsea, Bow and Spode are all types of what? **Porcelain**

12. Whom did Betty Boothroyd succeed as Speaker of the House? **Bernard Weatherill**

13. Who connects the archaeological programme *Time Team* with the comedy series *Blackadder*? **Tony Robinson**

14. Which king hid in an oak tree after the battle of Worcester? **Charles II**

15. What is the occupation of a leprechaun? **Cobbler**

16. Who wrote *Frenchman's Creek* and *My Cousin Rachel*? **Daphne du Maurier**

17. Who played Lex Luthor in the *Superman* films of the 1970s and 1980s? **Gene Hackman**

18. What was Capability Brown's Christian name? **Lancelot**

19. Where exactly in London were Frost Fairs held until 1831? **On the Thames**

20. Which character's chief opponent was Carl Peterson? **Bulldog Drummond's**

Quiz 158

1. Which car manufacturer designed Chris Boardman's gold-medal-winning bike? **Lotus**

2. In *The Screwtape Letters*, who was Screwtape? **A devil**

3. In which play does Gwendolyn Fairfax love Jack Worthing, who was found in a handbag as a baby? ***The Importance of Being Earnest***

4. What was the name of the Indian custom in which widows flung themselves on their husband's funeral pyres? **Suttee**

5. Which European king died in 1993? **King Baudouin (Belgium)**

6. Which controversial writer wrote *Time For a Tiger* and *The Kingdom of the Wicked*? **Anthony Burgess**

7. Which pop group had albums called *Nevermind* and *Bleach*? **Nirvana**

8. Which British skater won Olympic, European and World titles in 1976? **John Curry**

9. What was unusual about Derek Jarman's film *Sebastiane*? **Latin dialogue**

10. Who said: "The bowler's Holding, the batsman's Willey."? **Brian Johnston**

11. Of which country was Kim Il Sung Prime Minister and President for 46 years? **North Korea**

12. Which theory of combustion did Antoine Lavoisier demolish in the late 18th century? **Phlogiston Theory**

13. Who played the TV detective *Banacek*? **George Peppard**

14. Which fashion designer designs under the Emporio label? **Armani**

15. Would you find a dossal in a church, a boarding house or a stable? **In a church (ornamental hanging)**

16. Which English county's emblem is an imp? **Lincolnshire's**

17. In Norse mythology, who rode a horse called Sleipnir? **Odin**

18. What is the capital of Pakistan? **Islamabad**

19. What would you do with a tulwar? Would you cook on it, fight with it or keep maps in it? **Fight (It's a sword.)**

20. What name was given to the 4th Arab-Israeli War (1973)? **Yom Kippur War**

Quiz 159

1. Who would a jerquer work for? A textile factory, Customs and Excise or a riding academy? **Customs and Excise**

2. Which duo's theatrical performances were called *At the Drop of a Hat*? **Flanders and Swann's**

3. Who played the title role in the film *Shirley Valentine*? **Pauline Collins**

4. Which part of the body is affected by otitis? **The ear**

5. Who was the founder of the Sikh religion? **Nanak**

6. In which country are the Tagalog a major ethnic group? **Philippines**

7. Which country won the Men's World Cross Country Championship from 1989 to 1994? **Kenya**

8. Which of these countries does NOT drive on the left: New Zealand, Cyprus, Sweden or South Africa? **Sweden**

9. What name is given to a pillar or supporting column in the shape of a woman? **Caryatid**

10. Inguri, Nurek and Guavio are among the world's highest what? **Dams**

11. In which film did Harrison Ford come from the future to destroy android Rutger Hauer? ***Blade Runner***

12. Which singing voice is between tenor and soprano? **Alto**

13. In which country did the lambada dance originate? **Brazil**

14. In what would a Ricardian be interested? **Economics**

15. Which series of UK satellites was launched by the USA from 1962 to 1979? **Ariel**

16. Fullerenes, discovered in 1985, were a new form of which element? **Carbon**

17. Which European Prime Minister was assassinated in February, 1986? **Olaf Palme**

18. What is measured on the pH scale? **Acidity/Alkalinity**

19. What is the traditional dessert on Thanksgiving Day? **Pumpkin Pie**

20. What are caught in a kheda? **Elephants**

Quiz 160

1. Who said of Linford Christie: "He's a well balanced athlete. He's got a chip on each shoulder."? **Derek Redmond**

2. Who won the Tour de France for the third successive time in 1993? **Miguel Indurain**

3. Complete this literary quartet: Henry, Douglas, Ginger and . . . **(Just) William**

4. Who played Nora Charles in the *Thin Man* films? **Myrna Loy**

5. Who recorded albums called *Pandemonium Shadow Show* and *Pussy Cats*? **Nilsson**

6. Which former US First Lady worked as an editor for the publishers Viking and Doubleday? **Jackie Onassis**

7. Which fashion designer created the Space Age Collection in 1964? **Pierre Cardin**

8. Which drug is obtained from the Yellow Cinchona plant? **Quinine**

9. With what is the organisation CERN concerned? **Nuclear Research**

10. With which country do you associate tennis player Petr Korda? **The Czech Republic**

11. What do the Greeks call the Elgin Marbles? **Parthenon Marbles**

12. How many permanent members are there in the UN Security Council? **Five**

13. In which country is the TV News Agency Visnews based? **England**

14. In which African country do the Ashanti live? **Ghana**

15. Greek – men; Dutch – maand; German – monat; English – . . . (what)? **Month**

16. Which 1912 hoax regarding man's ancestry was not exposed until 1953? **Piltdown Man**

17. Which Oliver Stone war film won Best Picture Oscar in 1986? ***Platoon***

18. Which is the longest Classic race? **St Leger**

19. Which pop group's road manager was shot dead in 1986 in Northern Ireland? **Bananarama's**

20. What name is given to the cultivation of plants without soil? **Hydroponics**

Quiz 161

1. Name the host city of the 2000 AD Olympics. **Sydney**

2. Who was President of Nicaragua from 1981 to 1990? **Daniel Ortega**

3. Who was the first Conservative Prime Minister? **Robert Peel**

4. Which religion has the Kathina festival as a National Holiday? **Buddhism**

5. When it's 12 noon (GMT) in London, what time is it in Casablanca? **12 noon**

6. What is measured in Criths? **(Mass of) Gases**

7. Which country has the Leone as its unit of currency? **Sierra Leone**

8. What was the occupation during the French revolution of a tricoteuse? **Knitting**

9. For what does the abbreviation SJ stand? **Society of Jesus**

10. What are orts? **Fragments, odds and ends**

11. Kislev, Teveth, Sivan and Av are all what?
Months in the Jewish Calendar

12. How many decibels is the noise of busy traffic?
65-70

13. Who won the Booker Prize for *The Old Devils*?
Kingsley Amis

14. Who directed *The Quiet Man*, *Rio Grande* and *Stagecoach*? **John Ford**

15. With which sport would you associate Joe Montana? **American Football**

16. Who would use a Jacquard? An underwater explorer, a weaver or a gymnast? **Weaver**

17. Which painter gave his name to a shade of red?
Titian

18. What does the musical expression 'con fuoco' mean? **With fire**

19. The original King Kong met his fate on the Empire State Building. On which landmark did The Amazing Colossal Man come to grief? **Boulder (Hoover) Dam**

20. Whose first solo No 1 was *I'm Still Waiting*?
Diana Ross's

Quiz 162

1. In which newspaper did the strip cartoon *Jane* appear? ***The Daily Mirror***

2. In which British city is Usher Hall? **Edinburgh**

3. On which farm did Worzel Gummidge live? **Scatterbrook**

4. Which fictitious country was ruled by the Elphbergs? **Ruritania**

5. Who was the first man to drive at more than 400 mph? **John Cobb**

6. Who played the title role in *Young Winston*? **Simon Ward**

7. Who is the patron saint of messengers? **St Gabriel**

8. Who recorded albums called *Hounds of Love*, *Never For Ever* and *The Whole Story*? **Kate Bush**

9. After a gap of many years a new *Carry On* film was made in 1992. What was it called? ***Carry On Columbus***

10. Who wrote *Ode To the West Wind*? **Shelley**

11. In Welsh folklore, who were Tylwyth Teg? **Fairies**

12. When Wolfe took Quebec, which general did he defeat? **Montcalm**

13. Which horse won the 1993 Grand National? **There was no winner!**

14. Where does a breast buffer work? **In a shoe factory**

15. Which film was made from the book *The Small Woman*? ***The Inn of the Sixth Happiness***

16. If you ordered 'caneton' in a French restaurant, what would you get? **Duck**

17. Which country was ruled by William the Lion? **Scotland**

18. Who played Dr Owen in the TV series *Owen MD*? **Nigel Stock**

19. What name is given to the period between Napoleon's escape from Elba and his defeat at Waterloo? **The Hundred Days**

20. In which classic novel did Inspector Javert hunt down Jean Valjean? ***Les Misérables***

Quiz 163

1. Which famous person was born Billy Blythe in 1946? **Bill Clinton**

2. In an interview with Oprah Winfrey in 1993 whom did Michael Jackson say he was in love with? **Brooke Shields**

3. Who accompanied Sir Ranulph Fiennes on his 95 day trek across Antarctica in 1993? **Dr Michael Stroud**

4. What in 1946 was ENIAC? **World's First Electronic Computer**

5. For which 1992 film did Clint Eastwood win best Director Oscar? ***Unforgiven***

6. Who led the Branch Davidian sect which was largely destroyed in a fire at Waco in Texas? **David Koresh**

7. Which tennis star was stabbed during a match in Hamburg? **Monica Seles**

8. With which song did Niamh Kavanagh win the Eurovision Song Contest? ***In Your Eyes***

9. The jackdaw, rook and crow belong to which genus of birds? ***Corvus***

10. Which country is surrounded by South Africa, Zimbabwe, Zambia, Angola and Namibia? **Botswana**

11. Which country won the 1992 World Cup Cricket final? **Pakistan**

12. What position was held by John Smith before he became Labour leader? **Shadow Chancellor**

13. Who said: "All I had to say to the RAF was 'Can you find me a pair of size fourteens?' "? **Terry Waite**

14. Which TV series had characters called Daphne Manners, Hari Kumar, Ronald Merrick and Barbie? ***The Jewel in the Crown***

15. Who wrote *The Fallen Idol* and *The Quiet American*? **Graham Greene**

16. What does the Dorcas Society provide? **Clothes for the poor**

17. Who co-composed the *Liverpool Oratorio* with Carl Davis? **Paul McCartney**

18. Legend says that if you throw a coin into the Trevi fountain in Rome, what will happen? **You'll return to Rome**

19. Whom did Judy Nelson sue for palimony? **Martina Navratilova**

20. Who said: "Boxing's just show business with blood."? **Frank Bruno**

Quiz 164

1. Who composed *The Tales of Hoffman*? **Offenbach**
2. Which film star said: "People think I have an interesting walk. Hell, I'm just trying to hold my gut in."? **Robert Mitchum**
3. Flopsy, Mopsy and Peter were three of Mrs Rabbit's children. Who was the fourth? **Cottontail**
4. What's the difference between 4 square miles and 4 miles square? **12 square miles**
5. With which island did Britain fight a war in 1896 that lasted only 38 minutes? **Zanzibar**
6. The names of which two countries are hidden in this sentence: 'Give a dog a bone and give him a little water.'? **Gabon and Mali**
7. If you order 'rognons' in a restaurant what will you get? **Kidneys**
8. Who painted *The Starry Night*? **Van Gogh**
9. Who played the lead in the films *Finders Keepers*, *Two a Penny* and *Take Me High*? **Cliff Richard**
10. Who had Top Ten hits with *Detroit City*, *I'm Coming Home* and *Help Yourself*? **Tom Jones**
11. Where would a vaporetto ply its trade? **On the canals of Venice**
12. Musically, where would you find a clarabella? **On an organ (It is a stop.)**
13. In medicine, what was Jarvik 7? **The first successful artificial heart**

14. In which Arkansas town in 1957 did integration in schools cause riots? **Little Rock**

15. Who is the chief god in Norse mythology? **Odin**

16. In which county are The Royal Botanic Gardens, at Kew? **Surrey**

17. On which island did the dodo live? **Mauritius**

18. Who wrote the plays *The Admirable Crichton*, *Quality Street* and *What Every Woman Knows*? **J M Barrie**

19. Which English king won the Battle of Edington in 878 AD? **Alfred the Great**

20. Which cricketer, knighted in 1975, has the middle names St Aubrun? **Gary Sobers**

Quiz 165

1. What does a mahout drive? **An elephant**

2. Of what do biltong, jerky and pemmican consist? **(Dried/preserved) Meat**

3. Who said: "I look upon the world as my parish."? **John Wesley**

4. What was the surname of the great showman whose Christian names were Phineas Taylor? **Barnum**

5. What is the other name of the plant Veronica? **Speedwell**

6. What is a porbeagle? **A shark**

7. Who created the character of Sancho Panza? **Cervantes**

8. When the farthing was still legal tender, in how many ways was it possible to have threepence, apart from a threepenny bit? **16 (Work it out!)**

9. Which is the odd one out of these: blenny, gar, wrasse, cushat and alewife? **Cushat (It is a bird – others are fish.)**

10. How many notes are in a double octave? **Fifteen**

11. Which tree produces the seeds from which cocoa is prepared? **Cacao**

12. What do you do if you genuflect? **Bend the knee, kneel**

13. What is another name for the plover or peewit? **Lapwing**

14. What hobby or skill would you practise on a tambour? **Embroidery**

15. If you were dysthymic, would you be wheezing, depressed, unable to swallow or dead? **Depressed**

16. If the right hand page is the recto, what is the left? **Verso**

17. Can you name either of the two teams who featured in the first broadcast football match, an FA Cup match in January, 1927? **Corinthians or Newcastle United**

18. What does a squaloid creature resemble? **A shark**

19. Which word was coined by Samuel Foote as a mocking title for a self-important person? **Panjandrum**

20. Which singer was known as the Prince of Wails and the Nabob of Sob? **Johnny Ray**

Quiz 166

1. What French name was given to the agreement reached between the UK and France in 1904? ***Entente Cordiale***

2. Who painted *Green Stripe*, *Red Studio* and *Dance and Music*? **Henri Matisse**

3. Which edible plant is also known as Lady's Finger or kidney vetch? **Okra**

4. Was primero a card game, a time of day or a prayer? **A card game**

5. What do the Scots call a wet mist or a sea fog? **A haar**

6. When *A Question of Sport* began, who was the question master? **David Vine**

7. What nationality was World Motor Racing Champion Jody Sheckter? **South African**

8. What is the collective name for a group of partridges? **Covey**

9. Who played the detective in *Who Framed Roger Rabbit?*? **Bob Hoskins**

10. Roger Fenton was famous for what during the Crimean War? **Photographs**

11. Fortnum and Mason began their famous hampers in 1851 to coincide with what? **The Great Exhibition**

12. In *The Wizard of Oz*, what was the lion seeking? **Courage**

13. With which event would you associate the slogan 'Not a penny off the pay, not a minute on the day'? **The 1926 General Strike**

14. What did John Herncastle steal in India in Wilkie Collins' famous novel? **The Moonstone**

15. What is the main attribute of an oleaginous substance? **Oil**

16. True or false: Fettes College is in Aberdeen? **False (It is in Edinburgh.)**

17. What are progeny? **Children, offspring**

18. What position was held by Donald Coggan from 1974 to 1980? **Archbishop of Canterbury**

19. Which English King was reputed to have written *Eikon Basilike*? **Charles I**

20. Who played John Wayne's leading lady in *The Quiet Man*, *Rio Grande* and *McLintock*? **Maureen O'Hara**

Quiz 167

1. Who was the cartoonist and musician who organised humorous musical concerts featuring strange instruments? **Gerard Hoffnung**

2. Who played the lead in the TV series *99-1*? **Leslie Grantham**

3. In which J B Priestley novel do three disparate characters form a professional concert party? ***The Good Companions***

4. Which cat was "the bafflement of Scotland Yard, the Flying Squad's despair"? **Macavity**

5. Is roxburghe a style of bookbinding, furniture inlay or Scottish dancing? **Bookbinding**

6. Who had Top Ten hits in the 1960s with *Sealed With a Kiss* and *Ginny Come Lately*? **Brian Hyland**

7. Which of King John's sons became king at the age of 9? **Henry III**

8. Who had a servant called Leporello, a wronged wife called Elvira and was handed over to devils by a statue? **Don Juan**

9. Which part of the body is usually affected by Raynaud's disease? **The fingers and hands**

10. For what type of paintings was Henry Raeburn famous? Portraits, horses or bible scenes? **Portraits**

11. After the Red Flag Act was repealed in 1896, what was the speed limit for road vehicles? Was it 10 mph, 12 mph or 15 mph? **12 mph**

12. Billingsgate was the former London fish market, but what is billingsgate? **Bad language**

13. What is oloroso? **Type of sherry**

14. Which chain of shops was begun by Terence Conran in 1964? **Habitat**

15. Which one word means a round timber, a lustrous mineral or solo boxing? **Spar**

16. Who had Top Ten hits with *Again*, *That's the Way Love Goes* and *Let's Wait Awhile*? **Janet Jackson**

17. In which country was disc jockey Alan Freeman born? **Australia**

18. Which book, now in Trinity College, Dublin, is an illuminated collection of the Four Gospels and was written in the 8th/9th centuries? ***The Book of Kells***

19. Who starred in the films *Cadillac Man*, *Awakenings* and *Toys*? **Robin Williams**

20. Who transformed conditions at Scutari, near Istanbul, in 1856? **Florence Nightingale**

Quiz 168

1. What is a quirt? Is it a curl, a trick or a whip? **A whip**

2. In which sport do teams compete for the Plunkett Shield, the Currie Cup and the Red Stripe Cup? **Cricket**

3. The foundations of which 16th century theatre were discovered in London in 1988? **The Rose Theatre**

4. Was sendal a silken fabric, a perfume or a hard wood? **A silken fabric**

5. Is an urubu a vulture, a gazelle or a porcupine? **A vulture**

6. Who, in cartoons, has for years been chased but never caught by Wile E Coyote? **Road Runner**

7. Margaret, the Maid of Norway, was Queen of which country from 1286 to 1290? **Scotland**

8. Discovered by Hans Hennig in 1899, what was RDX? **An explosive**

9. What nickname was applied to the literary character Arthur Chipping? **Mr Chips**

10. Who had Top Ten hits with *Angel*, *Gambler* and *Cherish*? **Madonna**

11. What was named after Dr David Anderson in 1938? **An air-raid shelter**

12. Apart from the Isle of Man, which other island has three legs as its emblem? Is it Sicily, Cyprus or Crete? **Sicily**

13. Who played Eleanor Bramwell in the TV series *Bramwell*? **Jemma Redgrave**

14. Little Moreton Hall is probably Britain's finest example of which kind of house? **Timber-frame**

15. Proverbially, what do you reap if you sow the wind? **The whirlwind**

16. In films, which historical character was played by Randolph Scott in *Frontier Marshal*, Henry Fonda in *My Darling Clementine* and Kurt Russell in *Tombstone*? **Wyatt Earp**

17. In which area of Italy is Chianti produced? **Tuscany**

18. What does it mean when pears and other fruits are said to be 'sleepy'? Are they ready to be picked, beginning to rot or are they windfalls? **Beginning to rot**

19. Which musical was based on H G Wells' novel *Kipps*? ***Half a Sixpence***

20. Where in Britain are the Standing Stones of Stenness? Are they in the Orkneys, the Shetlands or the Hebrides? **The Orkneys**

Quiz 169

1. Who wrote *Five Children and It*, *The Phoenix and the Carpet* and *Wet Magic*? **E Nesbit**
2. Which element has the chemical symbol Hg? **Mercury**
3. In cookery, which expression means 'firm when bitten'? **Al dente**
4. True or false: New York's underground system has more stations than any other? **True**
5. What term was applied to soldiers who were regarded as expendable in time of war? **Cannon fodder**
6. What word is used for a boxer who leads with his right? **Southpaw**
7. In 1959, what did Czech engineer Karel Drabal discover had the power to sharpen razor-blades and preserve food? **Pyramids**
8. Who directed the films *A Hard Day's Night*, *Juggernaut* and *Superman II*? **Dick Lester**
9. In *The Hitch-Hiker's Guide to the Galaxy*, what did the computer calculate was the answer to the meaning of life, the universe and everything? **42**
10. To the Americans it is a skimmer. What do the British call it? **A straw hat, a boater**

11. In *Uncle Tom's Cabin*, who, when asked where she came from, said: "I 'spect I grow'd."? **Topsy**

12. Whose trilogic autobiography was *Lark Rise To Candleford*? Was it Flora Thompson's, Laurie Lee's or Naomi Mitchison's? **Flora Thompson's**

13. When Robert the Bruce watched the spider, on which attempt did it succeed? Was it its 7th, 10th or 12th attempt? **7th**

14. With which TV series would you associate Doctors Greene, Ross, Lewis and Benton? ***ER***

15. Is a barrico a small barrel, a rampart or a hair-clasp? **A small barrel**

16. Who had Top Ten hits with *We Got a Love Thang*, *Finally* and *Keep On Walkin'*? **Ce Ce Peniston**

17. Which Chancellor of the Exchequer was forced to resign in 1947 because he leaked details of his budget before informing the House? **Hugh Dalton**

18. What French term is applied to crime films with a mood of cynicism, despair and corruption? ***Film Noir***

19. The Sphinx was made up of various creatures. What form did its head take? **Human**

20. True or false: Fauvism was a style of painting? **True**

Quiz 170

1. In the USA, who is Kriss Kringle? **Santa Claus**

2. Which toilet cleaner's advertising slogan was that it cleaned right round the bend? **Harpic**

3. Who is the patron saint of fishermen? **St Andrew**

4. Which one word means written permission to go through, to give up your option, and to go beyond? **Pass**

5. What does the Australian slang word 'yarra' mean? **Insane**

6. Who starred in the films *Intersection*, *Sliver* and *The Specialist*? **Sharon Stone**

7. Is kuru a seaweed, a disease or an antelope? **A disease**

8. In July 1923, how many US dollars were worth one million German marks: was it 1, 10 or 100? **1**

9. Who had No 1 hits with *See My Baby Jive* and *Angel Fingers*? **Wizzard**

10. Which word in radio communications means 'the message has been received and will be complied with'? **Wilco**

11. Which alphabet is known as 'futhark' or 'futhorc'? **Runic alphabet**

12. Who took over from Richard O'Brien as host of *The Crystal Maze*? **Ed Tudor-Pole**

13. What is the birthstone for January? **Garnet**

14. In which county is the seaside town of Westward Ho!? **Devon**

15. How many gold medals did Jesse Owens win in the 1936 Olympics? **4**

16. True or false: there is a place in Canada called Pugwash? **True**

17. Who married Aristotle Onassis in 1968? **Jackie Kennedy**

18. Which former Labour Leader was accused of being a Russian agent by *The Sunday Times*? **Michael Foot**

19. In which town did the Marsh Farm Estate riots of July 1995 occur? **Luton**

20. Alan Arkin, Ted Wass and Robert Benigni have all played which film detective? **Inspector Clouseau**

Quiz 171

1. Of what is a thrasonical person guilty? Boasting, religious zeal or extravagance? **Boasting**

2. Who said: "If God did not exist, it would be necessary to invent him."? **Voltaire**

3. Which famous Frenchman's wife was known as Tante Yvonne? **Charles De Gaulle's**

4. Who played Benton Fraser in the TV series *Due South*? **Paul Gross**

5. Does the term kyu come from kendo, judo or sumo? **Judo**

6. What was the pen name of Winifred Ashton who wrote *A Bill of Divorcement* and *Regiment of Women*? **Clemence Dane**

7. Which of these countries has a flag that is the reverse of the Polish flag? Is it Malaysia, Indonesia or Mongolia? **Indonesia**

8. Who had Top Ten hits with *Groovy Train* and *All Together Now*? **Farm**

9. Which poet wrote: "Ring out the thousand wars of old, Ring in the thousand years of peace"? **Tennyson**

10. Which fictional detective married Harriet Vane? **Lord Peter Wimsey**

11. Who, in a famous poem, was buried "darkly at dead of night"? **Sir John Moore**

12. True or false: the Olympic Flame was extinguished by a cloudburst during the 1984 Olympics? **False (1976 Olympics)**

13. In which country would you see most of the Kalahari Desert? **Botswana**

14. How many times did Ivan Lendl win the Men's Singles at Wimbledon? **None**

15. What collective term is used for the eight oldest universities in the USA? **Ivy League**

16. Gully Jimson, an eccentric artist, is the central character of which Joyce Cary novel? ***The Horse's Mouth***

17. Which country's royal family is the House of Bernadotte? **Sweden**

18. Which Eastenders actress appeared in the TV series *Split Ends*? **Anita Dobson**

19. Two British Prime Ministers have fought duels, one while in office. Name one of them. **Duke of Wellington or George Canning**

20. Which of the seven Wonders of the World was at Olympia? **Statue of Zeus**

Quiz 172

1. Who commanded the English troops at Culloden? **Duke of Cumberland**
2. What is the name of the Gulf formed between the heel and sole of Italy? **Gulf of Taranto**
3. What is the traditional Egyptian dance form rakshaki called in the Western world? **Belly dancing**
4. From which language do the words caviar, kiosk, tulip and yoghurt come? **Turkish**
5. Who, in films, has played Richard Hannay, Monte Cristo, Mr Chips, William Pitt and William Friese Greene? **Robert Donat**
6. What was the name of the theatre built by D'Oyly Carte to house the Gilbert and Sullivan operettas? **Savoy**
7. Whose 1994 Christmas No 1 was *Stay Another Day*? **East 17**
8. True or false: the HQ of Amnesty International is in New York? **False (London)**
9. What is the most abundant substance on Earth? **Water**
10. On a ship, is a sheet a sail, a spar or a rope? **A rope**
11. Who won Best Actor Oscar at the age of 76 for *On Golden Pond*? **Henry Fonda**

12. Phthisis is an old name for which disease? **Tuberculosis**

13. Who had Top Ten hits with *Invisible Touch*, *I Can't Dance* and *No Son of Mine*? **Genesis**

14. Which 1915 novel by D H Lawrence was banned as obscene and its central characters later re-appeared in *Women in Love*? ***The Rainbow***

15. What is measured on the Mercalli Scale? **Earthquakes**

16. In which US state is Three Mile Island, site of a nuclear accident in 1979? **Pennsylvania**

17. What peerage was Churchill offered when he retired in April 1955? **Dukedom**

18. What is the Earth's 'precession'? **Its wobble (on its axis)**

19. What is the unit of currency in Zaire? **The zaire**

20. In ancient times, what would you have done in an apodyterium? **Removed your clothes (before bathing)**

Quiz 173

1. Glima, kushti and schwingen are all forms of which sport? **Wrestling**

2. What name is given to the series of 15 elements from lanthanum (Atomic No 57) to lutetium (Atomic No 71)? **Lanthanides (or rare-earth metals)**

3. Which King of England was known as The Sailor King? **William IV**

4. True or false: the musical term giocoso means 'with fun'? **True**

5. Which ship carried the Pilgrim Fathers to America? **The *Mayflower***

6. In finance, what does PEP stand for? **Personal Equity Plan**

7. What name is given to the less spectacular cemetery to the south of The Valley of the Kings? **The Valley of the Queens**

8. Who put Peter Rabbit's father into a pie? ***Mrs* Macgregor**

9. Who wrote the four novels collectively known as *The Alexandria Quartet*? **Lawrence Durrell**

10. Was a jazey a servant, a wig or a chamber-pot? **A wig**

11. Who had six successive Top Ten hits including *Don't Cry*, *Live and Let Die* and *November Rain*? **Guns 'n Roses**

12. On which TV show did Sir Mortimer Wheeler become famous? ***Animal, Vegetable and Mineral***

13. Who starred in the films *Thelma and Louise*, *Lorenzo's Oil* and *The Player*? **Susan Sarandon**

14. William Gilbert, who wrote a famous book about magnetism, held which post at the courts of Elizabeth I and James I? **Royal Physician**

15. Who played the bumbling British spy in the TV series *The Top Secret Life of Edgar Briggs*? **David Jason**

16. What is the popular name for a lycanthrope? **Werewolf**

17. Who composed the music for *Star Wars*, *Jaws* and *Raiders of the Lost Ark*? **John Williams**

18. Which annual event is held in Ranelagh Gardens in London? **Chelsea Flower Show**

19. Which French writer wrote the *Claudine* books? **Colette**

20. From which city did Robinson Crusoe come? **York**

Quiz 174

1. True or false: Charleroi, Namur and Mons are all in France? **False (Belgium)**

2. What is the name for the written instructions sent by a solicitor to a barrister before a court hearing? **Brief**

3. Over which river was the world's first cast-iron bridge built? **River Severn**

4. What were named after American General Ambrose Burnside? **Sideburns**

5. Which director, universally regarded as making the cinema's worst films, was played by Johnny Depp in a 1994 film biography? **Ed Wood**

6. The ancients believed the body was made up of four humours. Blood and bile were two; name one other. **Phlegm or choler**

7. Christopher Timothy had a real life romance with his leading lady from *All Creatures Great and Small*. Who was she? **Carol Drinkwater**

8. What name is given to the annual ritual on the Thames when swans are given their owners' marks? **Swan-Upping**

9. Which well-known firm paid for a new wing built on the National Gallery and opened in 1991? **Sainsbury's**

10. In hurling, how many players are there on each side? **15**

11. Who wrote the play *Androcles and the Lion*? **G B Shaw**

12. What would be served at a Thyestean Feast? Human flesh, humble pie or salt-less food? **Human flesh**

13. Who created the detective Adam Dalgleish? **P D James**

14. Who had Top Ten hits with *Big Fun*, *Good Life* and *Ain't Nobody Better*? **Inner City**

15. Is a clerihew a member of the church, a poem or a plant? **A poem**

16. Who managed Huddersfield Town to three successive Football League titles in the 1920s? **Herbert Chapman**

17. True or false: Greece was ruled by Turkey until 1830? **True**

18. What was E M Forster's middle name? **Morgan**

19. Is crowdy a kind of cheese, a medicinal plant or a teacake? **A kind of cheese**

20. Which 17th century writer had a cousin Stankes, an Aunt James and a sister Pall? **Samuel Pepys**

Quiz 175

1. What would we call a corrida de toros? **A bullfight**

2. In India what are the 'social' classes called? **Castes**

3. What is Betty Boothroyd's constituency? **West Bromwich West**

4. Which monster was slain when the "vorpal blade went snicker snack"? **The Jabberwock**

5. Which military group were central to the film *Gung Ho!*? **US Marines**

6. Which Greek king was murdered by his wife Clytemnestra and her lover on his return from a long absence? **Agamemnon**

7. In which science was Amedeo Avrogado famous? **Physics**

8. Which one word means a horse, a basket and a swan? **Cob**

9. Nicholas I said: "Russia has two generals in whom she can trust." Can you name one? **January or February!**

10. Who wrote the novels *The Red Rover*, *The Pathfinder* and *The Pioneers*? **James Fenimore Cooper**

11. Who had Top Ten hits with *Celebration*, *Joanna* and *Get Down On It*? **Kool and the Gang**

12. What nationality is golfer Ian Baker-Finch? **Australian**

13. In which TV serial did Agent Cooper investigate the murder of Laura Palmer? ***Twin Peaks***

14. What are affected by phlebitis? **Veins**

15. In France, which of these is NOT a port? Brest, St Nazaire or Toulouse? **Toulouse**

16. True or false: Annie Oakley's first name was Phoebe? **True**

17. What is the domesticated polecat called? **Ferret**

18. Which religion has a sect called the Essenes? **Judaism**

19. Friedrich Wilhelm I, II, III and IV were kings of where from 1813 to 1861? **Prussia**

20. Who presented the TV programme *Eureka!*? **Matthew Kelly**